MathLand.

Journeys Through Mathematics

- ♦ Charles
- ♦ Randolph Brummett
- ♦ McDonald
- ♦ Westley

STUDENT RESOURCE BOOK

This book of ready-to-use student pages is taken directly from the MathLand RESOURCE MANAGER.

Use this unit-by-unit compilation of essential student pages with the MathLand program.

Family Letters

Daily Tune-Up Reviews

Unit Reviews

Computation Checks

Grid Paper

And More . . .

Creative Publications

Acknowledgments

Project Coordinator Nancy Homan
Editor Jeffrey Stiegel
Cover Design and Production Graphic Advantage, Ltd.
Manufacturing Dallas Richards

ISBN: 0-7622-1240-3
1 2 3 4 5 6 7 8 ML 05 04 03 02 01 00 99
Catalog No. 23511
Customer Service: 800-624-0822
http://www.creativepublications.com

MathLand Student Resource Book

GRADE 5

Contents

MathLand® Student Resource Book • Grade 5—23511
© Creative Publications

MathLand Student Resource Book

Contents *(continued)*

MathLand Student Resource Book

GRADE
5

Contents *(continued)*

Name _____

Sibling Statistics
Displaying and Analyzing Family Data

What you will do:

- Make a "sibling strip" to describe the children in your family.

- Organize the information around specific questions about your siblings.

- Create displays that let you share your findings.

- Find the average number of children and pets in the families of your entire class.

Name _____   Date Due _____

Dear Student,

This week we have been learning about our classmates and their brothers and sisters and displaying our findings on graphs and Venn diagrams. Here's a Venn diagram survey for you to do with your family, friends, and neighbors.

Home Work

Who Can Do...?

1. Choose three skills from the list shown. Label each of the Venn circles with the skills.

2. Write down your predictions about what you'll find out when you survey people about those skills.

3. Ask your family and friends which of the things they are able to do.

4. Record each person's response in the correct area of the Venn diagram. Write down some things the completed Venn diagram shows.

Skills
• Ride a bicycle
• Swim
• Snow ski
• Twirl a yo-yo
• Water ski
• Do a flip
• Roller skate
• Walk on stilts
• Stand on head

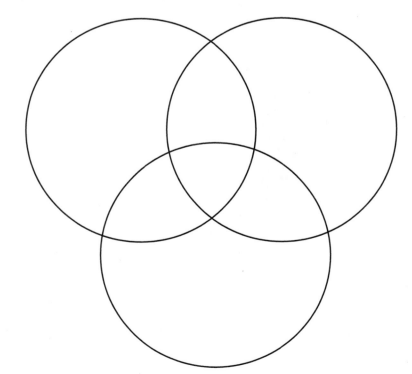

1-inch Grid

1-inch Grid

How to Make a Sibling Strip

1. Color a square for each child in your family, including you.

2. Color squares blue for boys and red for girls.

3. Number each square, beginning with 1 at the top. The numbers indicate the order of birth. Square 1 represents the oldest child, and so on.

4. Circle the number that indicates you in the family order. Put your initials in that square.

5. Cut out the strip.

Sibling Questions

- How many of us have more boys than girls in our family? more girls than boys?

- How many of us are the oldest children in our family? the youngest? somewhere in the middle?

- How many of us have brothers? sisters? both?

- How many of us have older siblings? younger? both?

- How many of us have no boys in our family? 1 boy? 2 boys? more?

- How many of us have no girls in our family? 1 girl? 2 girls? more?

Name _____

About Your Week

Comparison Polls
Designing, Conducting, and Interpreting Surveys

What you will do:

- Discuss the various groups within your school.

- Write survey questions about different topics.

- Predict the opinions of the various groups.

- Poll several of the groups.

- Analyze the surveys' results to compare the different groups.

- Create visual displays and share your findings with your classmates.

Name _____   Date Due _____

Dear Student,

This week we have been surveying different groups of
people in our school on various topics and comparing
the responses of one group to another. We've been
using charts, graphs, and diagrams to display our data.
See if you can find some information at home that
uses charts or graphs to communicate information.

Home Work

What Does It Say?

1. Look through newspapers and
    magazines at home.

2. Find a chart, graph, table, or diagram.

3. Cut out or copy the visual display.

4. Write a summary of things you can
    tell by analyzing the display.

5. Also write down any questions you
    have about the display.

6. Bring the display, your summary,
    and questions to school to share with
    the class.

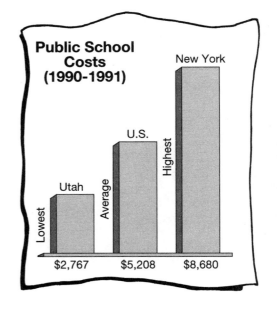

1-inch Grid

$\frac{1}{4}$-inch Grid

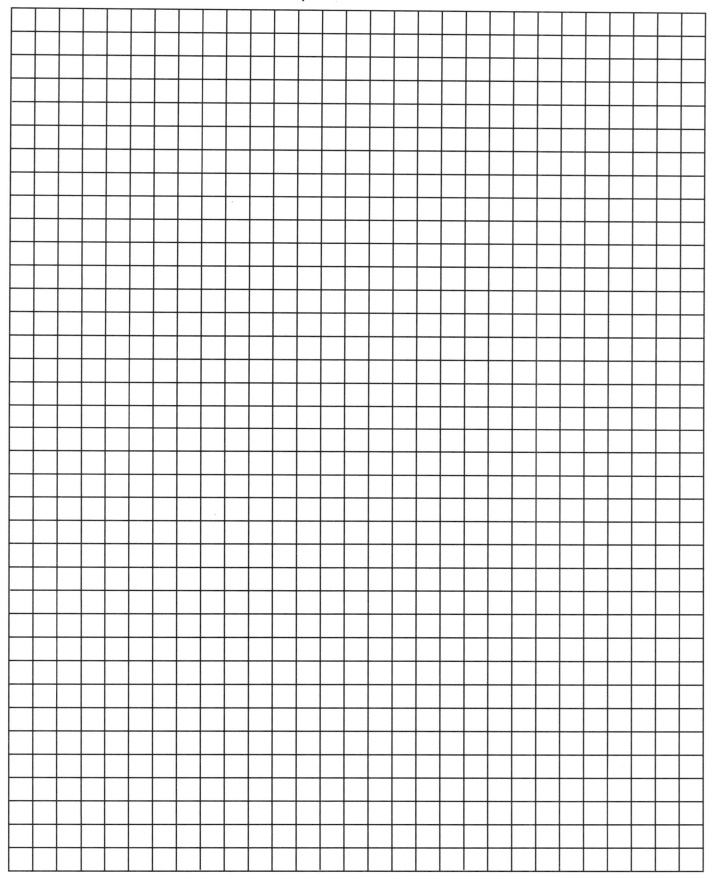

MathLand® Student Resource Book • Grade 5—23511

Name _____   Date _____

This graph shows the choices of toppings some fifth graders would want on pizza. The choices are: pepperoni, mushrooms, olives.

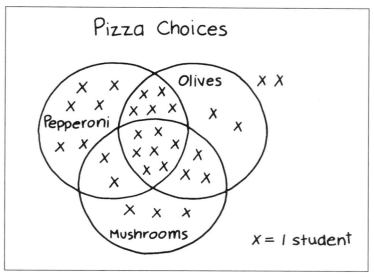

1. How many students would like the olive and mushroom combination? _____

2. What is a question that this graph cannot answer about this class's

   preferences for pizza toppings? _____

   _____

3. In a group of 4 students, 1 student has 5 family members, 1 student has 3 family members, 1 student has 8 family members, and 1 student has 4 family members. What is the average number of family members in this group of students? Use another sheet of paper to show your thinking.

Name _____

1 Unit Review

Mr. Grahn's students polled the fifth-grade classes to find out how many students would rather go camping and how many would rather go to an amusement park for the fifth-grade class trip. Here is a partially-completed graph:

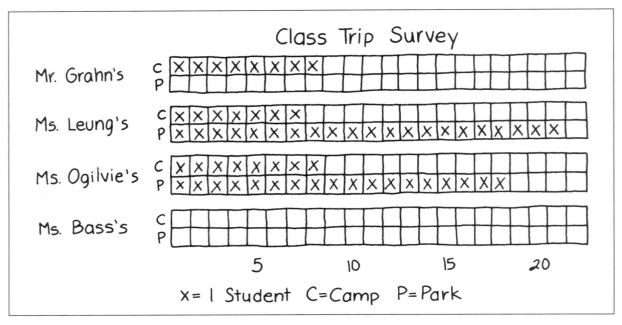

Class Trip Survey

Mr. Grahn's — C: XXXXXXXX P:

Ms. Leung's — C: XXXXXXX P: XXXXXXXXXXXXXXXXXXXXXX

Ms. Ogilvie's — C: XXXXXXXX P: XXXXXXXXXXXXXXXXXXX

Ms. Bass's — C: P:

5   10   15   20

x = 1 Student   C = Camp   P = Park

6. In Mr. Grahn's class, twice as many students voted to go to the amusement park as the number that voted to go camping. Add this data to the graph.

7. Ms. Bass's class is the same size as Mr. Grahn's class. In her class, three more students chose the amusement park than the number in Mr. Grahn's class. The rest chose camping. Add this data to the graph.

8. For which activity did the most students vote? _____

9. By how many votes did that activity win over the other choice? _____

MathLand® Student Resource Book • Grade 5—23511
© Creative Publications

1 Computation Check

Name _____   Date _____

Solve these problems as quickly as you can. Use the strategies that work best for you.

1. $12 \times 14 =$ _____   **2.** $254 - 25 =$ _____

3. $5\overline{)75}$ **4.** $\$30.00 \div 6 =$ _____

5. $17 \times 25 =$ _____   **6.** $121 \div 11 =$ _____

7. $\$0.49 \times 6 =$ _____   **8.** $\$4.44 \times 4 =$ _____

9. $3 \text{ cm} \times 15 \text{ cm} =$ _____   **10.** $8 \times 12 =$ _____

11. $25 \div 6 =$ _____   **12.** $\frac{1}{3} - \frac{1}{6} =$ _____

13. $\frac{1}{2} + \frac{1}{4} =$ _____   **14.** $12 \times 8 =$ _____

15.
$$\begin{array}{r} 355 \\ \times\ 32 \\ \hline \end{array}$$

16.
$$\begin{array}{r} 694 \\ +\ 535 \\ \hline \end{array}$$

17.
$$\begin{array}{r} \$53.00 \\ -\ 29.98 \\ \hline \end{array}$$

18.
$$\begin{array}{r} \frac{1}{10} \\ +\ \frac{3}{5} \\ \hline \end{array}$$

19.
$$\begin{array}{r} 54{,}035 \\ -\ 6{,}213 \\ \hline \end{array}$$

20.
$$\begin{array}{r} \frac{5}{8} \\ -\ \frac{1}{2} \\ \hline \end{array}$$

MathLand® Student Resource Book • Grade 5—23511
© Creative Publications

Growing Shapes
Investigating Patterns with Pattern Blocks

What you will do:

- Make a variety of shapes using same-shape Pattern Blocks.

- Keep a record of information about each square so that you can identify some patterns in the shapes you build.

- Make predictions based on the patterns you have observed.

- Use the patterns and predictions to solve a hexagon problem.

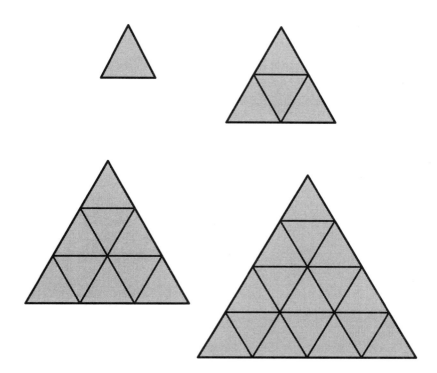

Name _____   Date Due _____

Dear Student,

This week we have been exploring patterns through Pattern Blocks. You may have noticed how beautiful some of your designs were. Here is your chance to create any design you want.

Home Work

Mosaic Design

1. Use the grid below to design a mosaic. You may choose to fill the grid or use only a part of it.

2. Your design should include a pattern that repeats at least three times, as well as other elements that are not part of the pattern.

3. Use any of the geometric shapes you have been working with this week in your design.

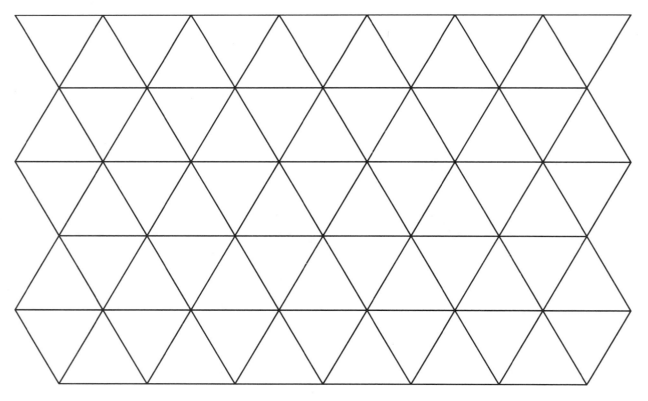

1-inch Grid

1-inch Grid

1-inch Grid

1-inch Grid

Triangle Grid

Name _____

Triangle Grid

Name _____

Triangle Grid

Name _____

〈28〉

Triangle Grid

Name _____

Growing Shapes Explorations

1. What patterns *do* you discover when you build growing triangles? Make a recording that shows what you found and explain the pattern. Make grid paper models or use a chart similar to the one you made with the class.

2. Try the exploration above using a different Pattern Block shape.

3. Compare the patterns you find for different Growing Shapes. How are the patterns alike? different? Report your findings.

4. How far can you go with a Growing Shapes pattern? Pick a shape and see what happens. Report on the patterns using words, sketches, or numbers. Predict as much as you can about the 10th, 50th, and 100th shape in the series. Use a calculator in this exploration if you'd like.

Hexagon Tilings

You Will Need:
- Pattern Blocks
- Triangular grid paper (*Resource Manager*, page 28)
- paper
- scissors

An artist wants to use tiles to create the largest design possible on the floor of a new train station. She wants her design to have repeating patterns of tiles. She has 36 hexagonal tiles, 36 diamond-shaped tiles, and 6 triangular tiles. Her design must be a hexagon.

Make recordings of the tile designs you create. Talk about your solutions.

100 Steps
Exploring Patterns of Sums

What you will do:

- Explore the pattern Karl Gauss used to find the sum of all the numbers from 1 to 100.

- Build a staircase using Rainbow Cubes to explore patterns for finding sums.

- Apply patterns you have observed to determine how many handshakes take place when 100 people are shaking hands.

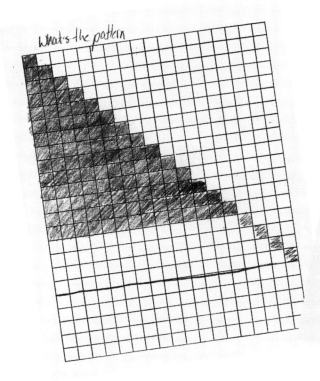

What's the pattern

With a one step the pattern is very easy to find. If you haven't already figured it out here is the pattern. The pattern goes in numerical order like 1,2,3,4,5,6,7,8,9,10 and so on each time you add one more.

Name _____

Date Due _____

Dear Student,

This week we are exploring more patterns, using them to make predictions and as useful problem-solving tools. Here are some patterns to think about.

Home Work

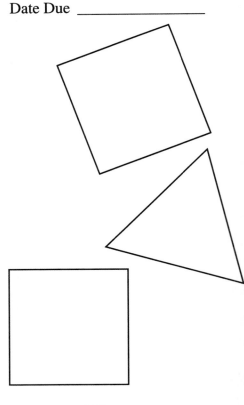

Square Numbers, Triangular Numbers

1. These numbers are called *square numbers:*

   1   (1×1)

   4   (2×2)

   9   (3×3)

   16 (4×4)

2. These numbers are called *triangular numbers:*

   1   (1)

   3   $(1 + 2)$

   6   $(1 + 2 + 3)$

   10 $(1 + 2 + 3 + 4)$

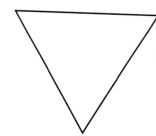

3. Can you figure out why the numbers have these names? (**Hint:** Try building some models.)

$\frac{1}{4}$-inch Grid

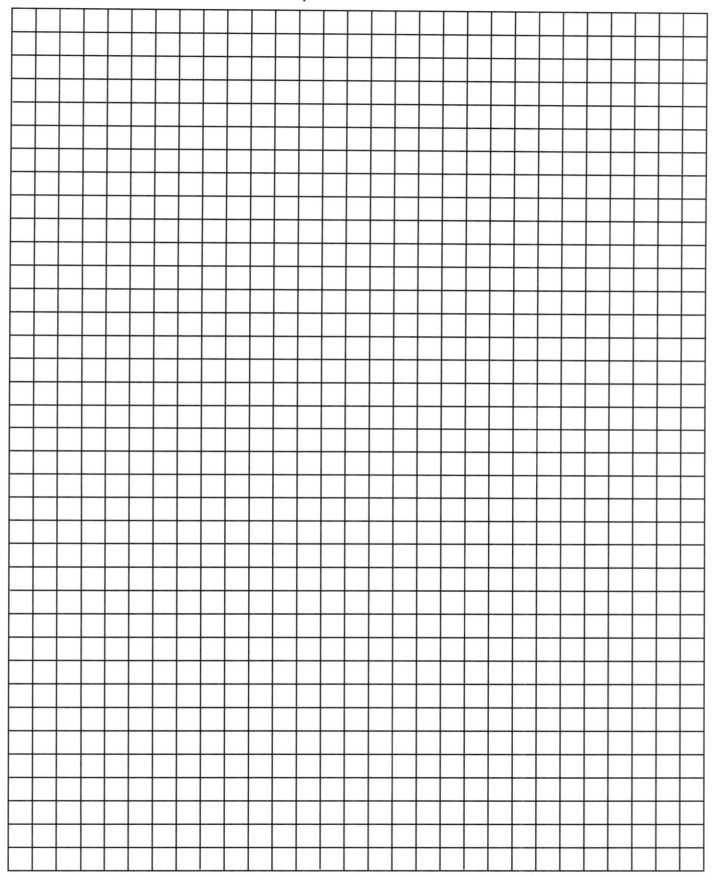

$\frac{1}{4}$-inch Grid

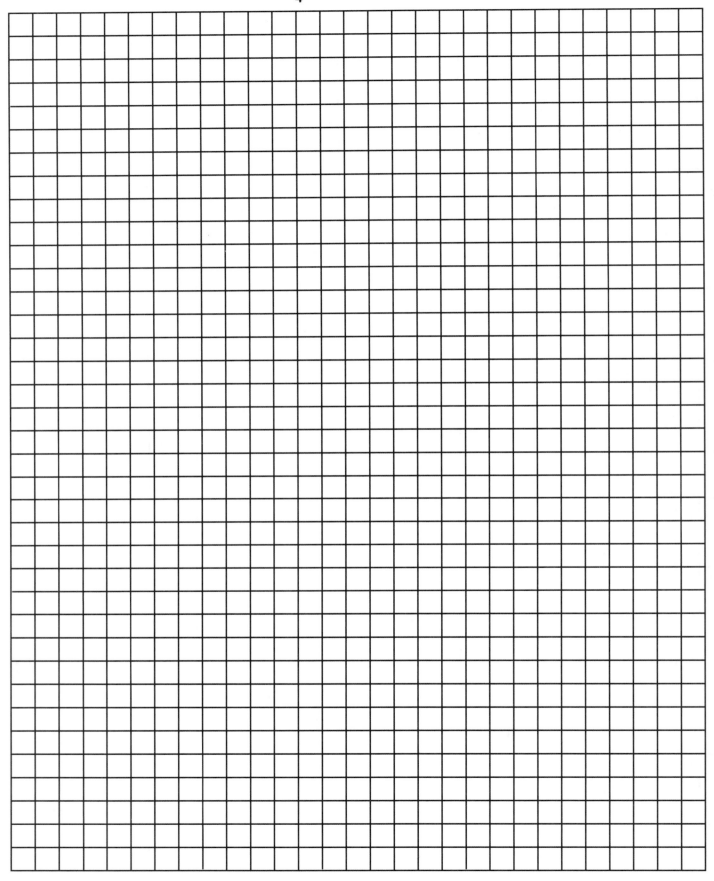

Staircase Explorations

Name _____

1. Build several single-step staircase models. Record the patterns you see. What are all the things you can say about a staircase with 100 steps?

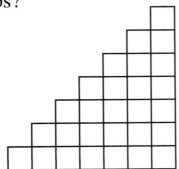

2. Build several double-step staircase models. Record the patterns you see. What are all the things you can say about a staircase like this with 100 steps?

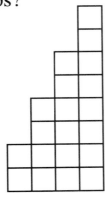

3. Build several "stile" single-step staircases. Record the patterns you see. What are all the things you can say about a staircase like this that is 100 steps high?

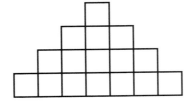

MathLand® Student Resource Book • Grade 5—23511
© Creative Publications

Name _____   Date _____

1. Write the name of this shape. _____

2. Which fraction below is read five fourths?

   A $\frac{1}{4}$

   B $\frac{4}{5}$

   C $\frac{5}{5}$

   D $\frac{5}{4}$

3. 27 students are going to the zoo. There is room for 4 students in each car.

   How many cars are needed? _____

4. What number comes next?

   34, 41, 48, 55, _____

5. Write the number the blocks show. _____

   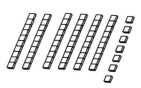

6. How is 29,648 read?

   A   two thousand, nine hundred six forty-eight

   B   two thousand, six hundred forty-eight

   C   twenty-nine thousand, six hundred forty-eight

   D   twenty thousand, nine hundred forty-eight

7. How is $42.09 read?

   A   forty-two dollars and ninety cents

   B   forty dollars and twenty-nine cents

   C   forty-two dollars and nine cents

8. What is one third of 18? _____

9. What is the next number?

   61,097   61,098   61,099   _____

10. How is $120.04 read?

   A   one hundred twenty dollars and four cents

   B   one hundred twenty-four dollars

   C   one hundred dollars and twenty-four cents

Name _____   Date _____

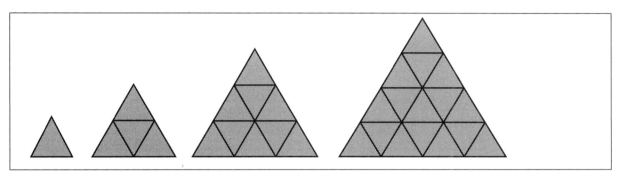

1. Here is part of a Growing Triangles pattern. Use words to describe at least three patterns that exist in the Growing Triangles.

2. How many blocks are needed to build the tenth triangle?

3. For any growing block pattern using Pattern Blocks, you can find a pattern in:
   A   the total number of blocks needed to build each figure
   B   the number of blocks added to build each new figure
   C   the perimeters of the figures
   D   only A and C
   E   A, B, and C

Use another sheet of paper to answer these questions.

4. Emilio has 43 blocks with which to build a single-step staircase. Explain how he could use a pattern to find out without building or sketching how high he can make the staircase.

5. When Emilio finishes making the staircase above, how many blocks will he have left over?

6. Explain how you can use a pattern to find the sum of all the odd numbers between 1 and 100.

7. These dots show that 4, 9, and 16 are all square numbers.

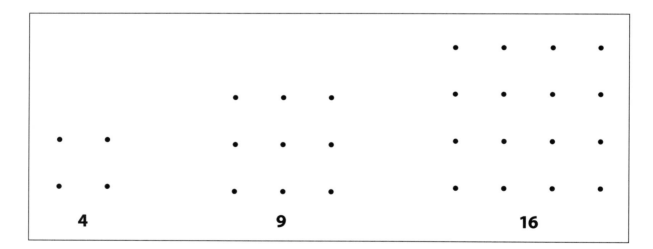

Is 49 also a square number? Prove your answer.

Remember This!
Focusing on Memorization Techniques

What you will do:

Day Trip One:
- Begin to identify the facts you know and the facts you still need to memorize.

Day Trip Two:
- Share your own memory tricks and learn some new ones from your classmates.

Day Trip Three:
- Learn one more trick for the ten hardest-to-remember facts.

Day Trip Four:
- See the facts in your mind and repeat them as you try to overcome obstacles that challenge your memory.

Day Trip Five:
- String as many facts together as possible and try to remember them all.

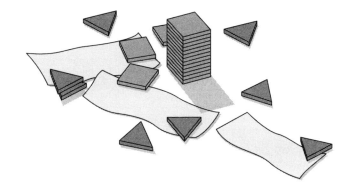

Family Letter

Name _____   Date Due _____

Dear Student,

This week you have been focusing on memorizing
your arithmetic facts. You paid special attention to
those facts that were difficult for you.

Home Work

Memory Techniques

1. Throughout the week, record the facts
   you are trying to memorize.

2. Write about the things you do to help
   you memorize your facts. Do you say
   the fact over and over? Do you have
   someone quiz you? Do you write the
   fact several times? Do you make a
   rhyme with it?

3. Write about your strategies for
   memorizing your arithmetic facts.

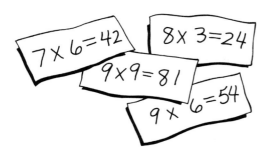

Finger Multiplication

1. To learn the nines facts, hold both hands out in front of you.

2. Start at the left. Count the fingers of the number you want to multiply 9 by. Bend down that finger. For example, for 9 x 7 your fingers should look like this:

3. To read the answer, think of the fingers to the left of the bent finger as tens. Think of the fingers to the right of the bent finger as ones. In the example above, the 6 fingers to the left of the bent finger represent 6 tens, or 60. The 3 fingers to the right represent 3 ones. That's 63.

4. When multiplying facts from 6 x 6 to 8 x 8, use this strategy. Hold both fists out in front of you. Think of each palm as 5. To represent a factor of 6, 7, or 8, raise the number of fingers that make that number when added to 5.

5. Use each hand to represent one of the factors in the problem. For example, to solve 7 x 8, show the 7 with your left hand and the 8 with your right hand.

6. To read the answer, think of the raised fingers as tens. Then multiply the number of bent fingers on the left hand by the number of bent fingers on the right hand to find the ones. In the problem shown above, the 5 raised fingers represent 50 and the 3 x 2 bent fingers equal 6, so 7 x 8 equals 50 + 6, or 56.

Name _____

Day Trip Four

Towers Up

You Will Need
- 2 players
- 14 Pattern Blocks (7 squares and 7 triangles)
- student-made fact strips
- paper
- pencils

1. Each player studies two of his own fact strips. When the facts are memorized, he hides the strips.

2. When both players are ready, they build a tower with the Pattern Blocks, taking turns placing blocks on the stack.

3. When the tower is complete, the players write their facts on the paper.

4. Repeat the game with different facts.

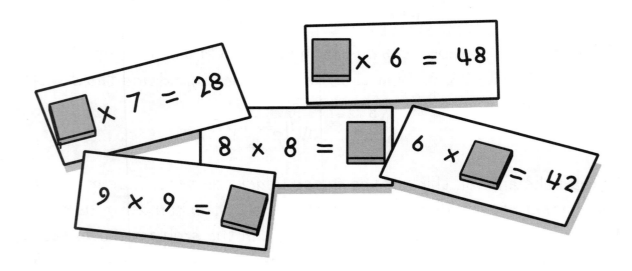

Blackout

You Will Need
- 2 players
- student-made fact strips
- 5 Pattern Block squares per player

1. One player selects five strips, places them between the two players, studies them, and then hides her eyes.

2. The other player covers one of the numbers in each equation with a Pattern Block square, counts silently to 20, and then taps her partner on the shoulder.

3. The first player opens her eyes and says each fact including the hidden number.

4. Players repeat the game with their facts, taking turns covering numbers.

Secret String of Facts

You Will Need
- 1 player
- 5 or more fact strips with answers folded under

1. Lay the facts out in a row. Look at one fact. Check the answer. Then hide the answer and repeat the fact to yourself several times.

2. Add a second fact strip to the string and follow the same process as in step 1. Try to say both facts, over and over, until you are ready to add another.

3. Continue until you think the string of facts is as long as you can remember. Then put your hand on your head and practice silently.

4. When the teacher comes to you, read your secret string of facts out loud.

5. Then mix up the facts, lay them out in a different order, and work on the new string of facts.

Name _____

Alternative Algorithms
Investigating Alternative Methods
of Multiplication and Division

What you will *do*:

• Investigate ancient Russian and Egyptian multiplication algorithms.

• Use Base Ten Blocks to help develop visual images for solving two-digit multiplication problems.

• Use Base Ten Blocks to help develop visual images for solving division problems.

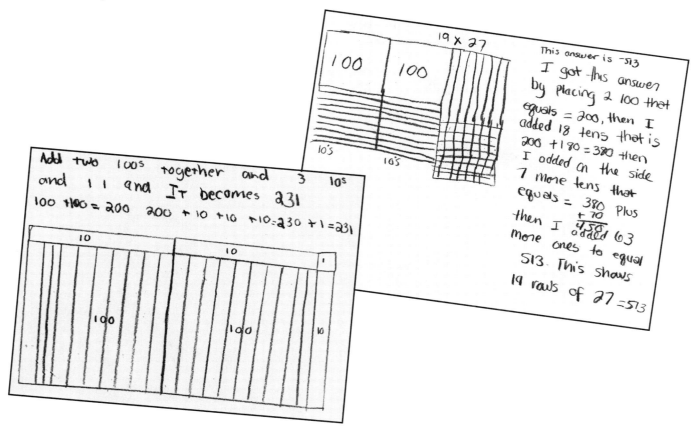

Family Letter

Name _____   Date Due _____

Dear Student,

This week you have been exploring new strategies for solving two- and three-digit multiplication and division problems. You have learned some ancient algorithms and have used Base Ten Blocks to solve problems. For homework, find out how a family member solves a three-digit multiplication problem.

Mom, here's a problem for you: 123 x 315. Show me the steps you'd use to solve it.

Home Work

What's Your Algorithm?

1. Interview an older family member about their method for solving the problem: 123×315.

2. Have the family member show you the steps he or she used to solve the problem. Record the steps.

3. Use those same steps and try to solve another multiplication problem.

Russian Peasant Multiplication Algorithm 21 × 19

1. Make two columns on your paper. Label the first column "Halving" and the second column "Doubling." Write the first number under "Halving" and the second number under "Doubling."

2. Halve the first number until you reach one, writing the answer each time in the first column. Disregard any remainders.

3. Double the second number, writing the answer each time in the second column. Do this the same number of times it took you to halve the first number.

4. Draw a line through each row that has an even number in the "Halving" column.

5. Add the numbers in the "Doubling" column that do *not* have a line drawn through them as in the example below:

Halving		Doubling	
21	×	19	
~~10~~		~~38~~	("Halving" number is even.)
5		76	
~~2~~		~~152~~	("Halving" number is even.)
1		304	

Add: 19 + 76 + 304 = 399

21 × 19 = 399

Egyptian Multiplication Algorithm 69 × 19

1. Write the first number you are multiplying in the first column. Say to yourself, "That's 1 of it." Write this in the second column.

2. Add the first number from above to itself and write the equation in the first column. Say to yourself, "That's 2 of them." Write this in the second column.

3. Add the sum from above to itself and write the equation in the first column. Say to yourself, "That's 4 of them." Write this in the second column.

4. Add the sum from above to itself and write the equation in the first column. Say to yourself, "That's 8 of them." Write this in the second column.

5. Continue this pattern (1, 2, 4, 8, 16, 32, 64, 128,...) until you say to yourself a number that is greater than the second number you are multiplying. In the example, this number is 32 because 32 is greater than 19.

69	That's 1 of it.
69 + 69 = 138	That's 2 of them.
138 + 138 = 276	That's 4 of them.
276 + 276 = 552	That's 8 of them.
552 + 552 = 1104	That's 16 of them.
1104 + 1104 = 2208	That's 32 of them.

6. Now, find a way to add the numbers you've been writing in the second column so that the sum is exactly the second number you are multiplying, which in this example is 19.

$$16 + 2 + 1 = 19$$

7. Find the corresponding sums in the first column and add them together.

$$1104 + 138 + 69 = 1311$$

$$69 \times 19 = 1311$$

Name _____

About Your Week

Convince Us!
Using Mental Strategies to Solve Arithmetic Problems

What you will do:

- Use mental arithmetic to solve addition, subtraction, multiplication, and division problems.

- Tell the answers to the problems and explain the thinking you used to find the answers.

- Use Base Ten Blocks and mental arithmetic to solve the same problems in different ways.

Name _____   Date Due _____

Dear Student,

This week you have been constructing your own rules for adding, subtracting, multiplying, and dividing numbers. You have described your own thinking to convince the class (and yourself) that your way of getting an answer really works. Also, you have been using Base Ten Blocks to solve problems, focusing on division problems. For homework, show your family how to play Convince Me!

Here is one way to solve $110 \div 5$.
$100 \div 5$ is 20.
$10 \div 5$ is 2.
$20 + 2$ is 22.

Home Work

Convince Me!

1. Make up and write down ten problems, some of which are division problems. Make a few of them tricky. Write the answers.

2. Now show your problems to someone in your family. Say, "Choose any of these problems and I will tell you two different ways to prove that my answer is correct."

3. Write the two ways you used to solve each problem.

4. Bring this homework paper back to school and include it in your portfolio.

5. Show off your good thinking to different members of your family.

About Your Week

Calculator Investigations
Exploring the Calculator as a Problem-Solving Tool

What you will do:

Day Trip One:
- Use a calculator to play with numbers that would be too difficult to manage if you had to do all the calculation on paper.

Day Trip Two:
- Use the constant function on your calculator to hide a secret rule for your partner to find. Use mental arithmetic to figure out the rule.

Day Trip Three:
- Tackle a problem using the calculator and discover that you get decimal numbers on the display.

Day Trip Four:
- Find all kinds of interesting number patterns by using your calculator.

Day Trip Five:
- Try to figure out a mystery number using your calculator and various clues.

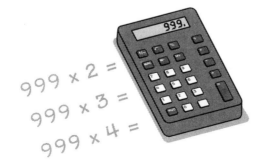

Name _____   Date Due _____

Dear Student,

This week you have been learning about calculators. You have learned that calculators can help you see patterns that would take a long time to find using paper and pencil. The calculator also lets you explore ways of working with larger numbers. The calculator allows you to try many different ways of solving a problem.

Home Work

Calculator Capers

1. Write a funny story, real or make-believe, about someone's experience using a calculator or about a time when someone should have used a calculator.

2. Your story should show that there are times when a calculator is an efficient tool for solving mathematics problems and other times when it is not so efficient.

Puzzle Bank

A. Use the digits 1, 2, 3, 4 to get the greatest possible product.

B. Use the digits 1, 2, 3, 4 to get the smallest possible product.

C. Use the digits 3, 4, 5, 6 to get the product closest to 2500.

D. Use the digits 5, 6, 7, 8, 9 to get the smallest product.

E. Use the digits 0, 3, 4, 6, 8 to get the quotient that is closest to 5.

F. Use the digits 1, 4, 6, 7, 8 to get the quotient that is closest to 50.

How to Play The Secret Rule

How to Play The Secret Rule

1. Partners need a calculator and paper.

2. Player A decides on a secret rule and enters in the calculator the following sequence: $\boxed{+}$ (or $\boxed{-}$), the number, $\boxed{=}$. (For the secret rule "add 5 to a number," the sequence is: $\boxed{+}$ 5 $\boxed{=}$.)

3. Next, Player A hides the secret rule by entering any number and pressing $\boxed{=}$.

4. Player B tries to find the secret rule by entering any number and pressing $\boxed{=}$. Player B records the number entered and the number that appears on the calculator display.

5. Player B continues entering numbers, pressing $\boxed{=}$, and recording until he is able to figure out the secret rule.

6. Partners switch roles and play again.

The Fine Number Nine

Use your calculator to complete the first three problems. Look for a pattern. Predict the answer to the fourth problem. Use your calculator to check the pattern. Test it with some problems of your own.

1. $99 \times 2 =$ _____

   $99 \times 3 =$ _____

   $99 \times 4 =$ _____

   Predict $99 \times 5 =$ _____

   What's the pattern?

2. $999 \times 2 =$ _____

   $999 \times 3 =$ _____

   $999 \times 4 =$ _____

   Predict $999 \times 5 =$ _____

   What's the pattern?

3. $9 \times 6 =$ _____

   $99 \times 66 =$ _____

   $999 \times 666 =$ _____

   $9999 \times 6666 =$ _____

   Predict $99{,}999 \times 66{,}666 =$ _____

   What's the pattern?

Mirror Image

Use your calculator to solve these problems. Look for a pattern and use the pattern to predict the answers. Verify the answers with your calculator.

1. $11 \times 11 =$ _____
   $11 \times 111 =$ _____
   $11 \times 1111 =$ _____
   Predict $11 \times 11{,}111 =$ _____
   What's the pattern?

2. $111 \times 111 =$ _____
   $111 \times 1111 =$ _____
   $111 \times 11{,}111$
   Predict $111 \times 111{,}111 =$ _____
   What's the pattern?

3. $6 \times 6 =$ _____
   $6 \times 66 =$ _____
   $6 \times 666 =$ _____
   Predict $6 \times 6666 =$ _____
   What's the pattern?

4. $6 \times 6 =$ _____
   $66 \times 66 =$ _____
   $666 \times 666 =$ _____
   Predict $6666 \times 6666 =$ _____
   What's the pattern?

5. $7 \times 7 =$ _____
   $7 \times 67 =$ _____
   $7 \times 667 =$ _____
   Predict $7 \times 6667 =$ _____
   What's the pattern?

6. $7 \times 7 =$ _____
   $67 \times 67 =$ _____
   $667 \times 667 =$ _____
   Predict $6667 \times 6667 =$ _____
   What's the pattern?

What's My Number?

1. My number multiplied 4 times by itself equals 625. What's my number?

2. My number multiplied by itself and then divided by 2 equals 8. What's my number?

3. My number divided by 5, minus 2, divided by 3 equals 6. What's my number?

4. My number multiplied by itself 4 times and then divided by 3 equals 432. What's my number?

5. My number doubled, then divided by 6 equals 4. What's my number?

6. My number halved 10 times equals 1. What's my number?

7. My number multiplied by itself 4 times equals 31,640,625. What's my number?

8. My number minus one half of itself, plus itself equals 75. What's my number?

9. My number multiplied by itself, minus itself equals 15,500. What's my number?

Name _____   Date _____

1. Write the missing number.

88, 80, 72, _____, 56

2. Write the fraction that is read:

four twelfths _____

seven fifths _____

3. Are these fraction pieces more than, less than, or equal to one whole?

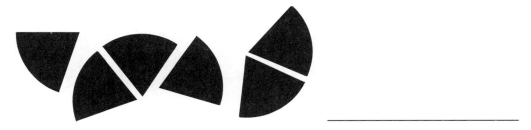

_____

4. How many inches are in $1\frac{1}{2}$ feet? _____

5. The length of a rope is 200 centimeters. How many meters long is it? _____

6. Write these in order from least to greatest.

7050, 7705, 7005 _____ _____ _____

7. In the circles, write the signs that make the equation correct.

(36 ◯ 4) ◯ 3 = 3

8. Write two numbers the answer falls between.

68 + 174 = ▢ _____ _____

9. What is the value of this group of coins? _____

10. Three blocks are covered. All the blocks show 143. Sketch the covered blocks.

Name _____

Strategy Show-Off
Applying Arithmetic Strategies to Games and Puzzles

What you will do:

• Use arithmetic strategies, pencil and paper, and your calculator to play a variety of games.

• Learn three challenging card games and use logical reasoning to develop effective game strategies.

• Use a variety of strategies to solve challenging arithmetic problems.

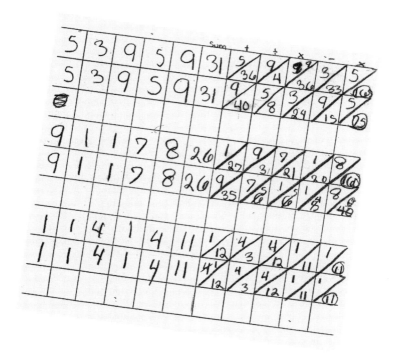

Name _____   Date Due _____

Dear Student,

This week you have been showing off your math strategies. You have been using your mental arithmetic abilities, paper and pencil, and calculator to help you solve some challenging problems. Use your strategies as you play this variation of High-Low Roller.

Home Work

High-Low Numbers

1. Use one-inch grid paper. Make a game board like the one used for High-Low Roller.

2. Use the numbers in your phone number and zip code to play the game.

3. Record your score.

4. At the end of the week, you'll compare your scores with the scores of your classmates.

Reckon™ Cards

1	**1**	**1**
2	**2**	**2**
2	**3**	**3**

Reckon™ Cards

3	3	4
4	4	5
5	5	6

MathLand® Student Resource Book • Grade 5—23511
© Creative Publications

Reckon™ Cards

6	**6**	**7**
7	**8**	**8**
8	**9**	**9**

Reckon™ Cards

9	**10**	**10**
11	**12**	**12**
13	**14**	**15**

Reckon™ Cards

16

16

17

18

18

19

20

21

22

Reckon™ Cards

23	**24**	**24**
25	**26**	**27**
28		**Wild Card**

MathLand® Student Resource Book • Grade 5—23511
© Creative Publications

Reckon™

You Will Need
• 2 players
• a deck of Reckon™ cards (*Resource Manager,* pages 59-64)

1. Each player is dealt three cards face down. Another card, the "answer" card, is placed face up in the center of the table.

2. The object is to be the first player to use two or three of the cards in her hand to make an equation (addition, subtraction, multiplication, or division) that equals the answer card.

3. If neither player can make an equation for the first answer card, then both players draw another card from the deck until one player can make an equation.

4. The first player to think of an equation places a hand over the answer card and tells the equation. If the equation is correct, the player scores a point.

5. Players then discard the cards they were using and deal themselves a new hand. Play continues for a set amount of time or until one player scores 10 points.

Name _____

Take Three

You Will Need
- 2 players
- a deck of Reckon™ cards (*Resource Manager*, pages 59-64)

1. One player deals 8 cards face up in 2 rows of 4. The remaining cards are placed face down in a stack.

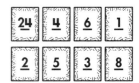

2. Player A forms as many 3-card equations (addition, subtraction, multiplication, or division) as possible using the 8 cards. Each card may be used in only one equation. Player A keeps the cards used to form equations.

3. Player A replaces the cards removed from the original 2 rows of 4 with cards from the draw pile, and it is Player B's turn to play.

4. Play ends when no further equations can be made. The player with the most cards wins the game.

Count Down

You Will Need
- 2 players
- a deck of Reckon™ cards (*Resource Manager, pages 59-64*)
- paper
- pencils

1. Each player is dealt 6 cards. The rest of the cards are placed face down in a stack.

2. The object is to be the first player to make 10 equations, using 2 or more cards for each equation. The first equation must equal 10, the second equation must equal 9, the third 8, and so on down to 1.

3. Each player, in turn, tries to make the appropriate equation by laying cards from his hand face up on the table and saying the equation. He replaces the cards that have been played with cards from the draw stack. Play then passes to the next player.

4. When a player cannot make an equation, he takes one card from the draw stack, and play passes to the next player.

5. The winner is the first to complete a set of equations equaling 10, 9, 8, 7, 6, 5, 4, 3, 2, and 1.

Name _____   Date _____

1. How would you use Base Ten Blocks to solve this multiplication problem:
16 × 22 = _____ ? Draw the blocks and explain your solution in writing.

2. How would you use Base Ten Blocks to solve this division problem:
93 ÷ 7 = _____? Draw the blocks and explain your solution in writing.

Name _____

Solve these problems in your head. Use words and numbers to explain how you thought about each problem in your head.

3. 13
   × 9

4. 417−209 = _____

5. Using the numbers 3, 4, and 7, write an equation that equals 5. Keep a record of your work.

Use a calculator to solve the problems on this page. Use another sheet of paper to keep a record of the calculations you try.

6. Using only the digits 3, 4, 5, 6, and 7, write the division problem that results in the smallest quotient.

7. Using only the digits 1, 3, 5, 6, and 7, write the division problem that results in a quotient as close to 30 as possible.

8. My number multiplied by itself 3 times equals 2197.

What's my number? _____

9. My number multiplied by 3, plus 9, divided by 7, equals 9. What's my number?

_____

10. My number multiplied by itself, minus itself,

equals 1260. What's my number? _____

Category Cards
Examining Variables in Attribute Sets

What you will *do*:

- Select the attributes for different sets of Category Cards of faces and houses.

- Work with a partner and select the attributes for an attribute set based on a category of your own choosing.

- Summarize the attributes for your set.

- With your partner create an attribute set of cards, showing all the possible combinations.

- Explore attribute card sets created by your classmates and write attribute summaries for them.

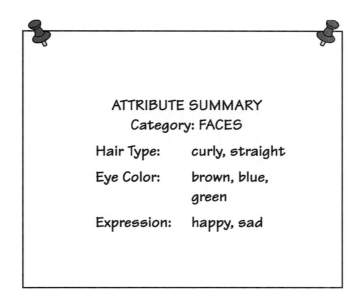

ATTRIBUTE SUMMARY
Category: FACES

Hair Type:	curly, straight
Eye Color:	brown, blue, green
Expression:	happy, sad

Family Letter

Name _____   Date Due _____

Dear Student,

This week you have been using your logical-thinking abilities. You have been making Category Cards and summarizing their attributes.

Home Work

Category Cards for the Family

1. Draw a different set of Category Cards to keep at home. Next week you can use them to teach your family some games. Before you begin, here are some things to think about:

   A. What theme or category do you want to pick for your cards?

   B. How many different attributes will there be? What are some of them?

   C. What are the options you'll want to use for each attribute?

   D. How many cards will there be all together in your set?

2. When your set is complete, bring it to class to share. But remember to take it home again. You'll need it there next week.

Name _____

Looking Back

Guess the Attributes

You Will Need
- 2 players
- one set of Category cards
- scratch paper
- pencils

1. Place the set of Category Cards face down in a stack.

2. Draw one card at a time. Look carefully at the card to learn all you can from it. Make a sketch or take notes of things that might be clues to the attributes and options in the set.

3. Continue turning over one card at a time and looking at it for clues until you think you and your partner know all the attributes and options for the set.

Labels and Links
Exploring Logical Operators: And, Or, Not

What you will *do:*

Day Trip One:
- Explore another pair of classmates' Category Cards sets and determine which cards are missing.

Day Trip Two:
- Create labels and logical "links" to describe subsets.

Day Trip Three:
- Use the labels and links you created to make logic puzzles to stump your classmates.

Day Trip Four:
- Use your Category Cards sets to play the "Guess My Card" game.

Day Trip Five:
- Using Venn diagram circles, you pick labels and links to define different subsets.

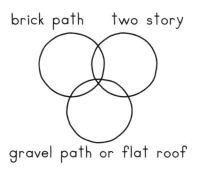

Family Letter

Name _____   Date Due _____

Dear Student,

This week you have been exploring sets of attribute
cards in a variety of ways, including playing games
with them. Try playing one of these games at home
using the Category Cards for the Family you made
last week at home.

Home Work

**Let's Play Category Cards
for the Family**

1. Read the rules for Hidden Cards and
   Guess My Card (*Resource Manager,*
   pages 75, 76). Teach your family
   the games.

2. After playing each game, write a
   summary about your experience to
   bring to class. How did the game go?
   Was the game hard or easy for your
   family? What did you know that
   they didn't?

Name _____

Hidden Cards

You Will Need
- 2 players
- a set of Category Cards
- paper
- pencils

1. Partners work together on this game. Open the bag and, without looking at the cards in the bag, remove all but 3 cards.

2. Carefully study the cards you removed and organize them in a way that will help identify the hidden cards that are still in the bag.

3. Sketch what you think the hidden cards are. Then look inside the bag to see if you were right.

Guess My Card

You will need
- 2 players
- a set of Category Cards
- scratch paper
- pencils

1. Place all the cards face up in random order on the table.

2. Secretly, without touching or indicating it in any way, Player A "chooses" a card and makes a sketch of it, keeping the sketch hidden.

3. Player B tries to guess which card was chosen by asking the fewest possible number of questions. Only yes or no responses are allowed. Player B may use and, or, and not in the questions.

4. Player A answers each question, and Player B removes any cards that the question has eliminated.

5. When Player B thinks he knows the answer, he makes a guess. If it matches the card Player A drew in the sketch, they reverse roles and play again.

Venn Diagram Explorations

You have been using label cards and the three "links" (and, or, not) to describe sorting rules and make logic puzzles. Use label and link combinations with three Venn circles for these activities:

- Find label and link combinations that let you place a lot of cards in the circles. Make a record of the combination that resulted in the most cards in the circles.

- Find label and link combinations that let you place very few cards in the circles. Make a record of the combination that resulted in the fewest cards in the circles.

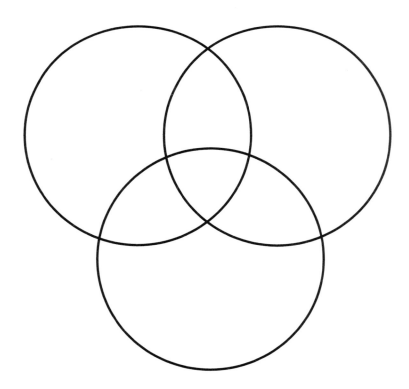

Name _____   Date _____

Use another sheet of paper to answer these questions.

1. Emilio was going to the theater with his class. He decided to dress up. He had the following choices of what to wear:

Ties:	**Pants:**	**Shirts:**
Striped	Brown	White
Solid	Black	Blue
Dotted		

   How many possible ways can Walter dress in pants, a shirt, and a tie? Explain in words and numbers how you know.

2. Four of the sixteen cards in this set of category cards are face down. Once they are turned over, each of the four categories will be complete. Draw the missing houses to complete the set.

⟨Q42⟩   MathLand® Student Resource Book • Grade 5—23511
© Creative Publications

Use the category cards on the previous page and the Venn diagram below to answer questions 3–6. Use another sheet of paper to record your answers.

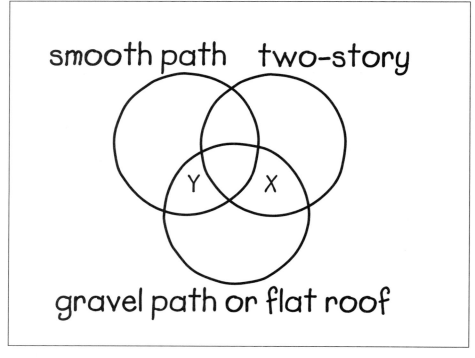

3. What are the labels and links (*and, or,* or *not*) for a house that goes where the **X** is?

4. Place an **A** in the section that fits these labels and links: *smooth path and peaked roof and not two story.*

5. Place a **B** in the section for a house with these labels and links: *smooth path and flat roof and three story.*

6. June said, "A house that would fit in the category marked by **Y** would have to have a flat roof. A house in the **X** section would not necessarily have a flat roof." Do you agree? Explain your answer.

Name _____   Date _____

Solve these problems as quickly as you can. Use the strategies that work best for you.

1. $3 \times 2 \times 2 =$ _____

2. $\$17.03 \times 14 =$ _____

3. $273 \times 26 =$ _____

4. $2{,}456 \div 16 =$ _____

5. $144 \div 12 =$ _____

6. $\$48.00 \div 12 =$ _____

7. $4 \times 3 \times 6 =$ _____

8. $\$24.35 + \$1.63 + \$0.46 =$ _____

9. $15 \times 12 =$ _____

10. $98 \div 9 =$ _____

11. $7\overline{)1421}$

12. $19 \times 38 =$ _____

13. $44 \div 7 =$ _____

14. $135 \div 6 =$ _____

15.
$$\begin{array}{r} 25 \\ \times\ 25 \\ \hline \end{array}$$

16.
$$\begin{array}{r} 28 \\ \times\ 7 \\ \hline \end{array}$$

17.
$$\begin{array}{r} \$10.45 \\ -\ 4.99 \\ \hline \end{array}$$

18.
$$\begin{array}{r} 145 \\ +\ 96 \\ \hline \end{array}$$

19.
$$\begin{array}{r} \$100.00 \\ -\ 78.13 \\ \hline \end{array}$$

20.
$$\begin{array}{r} 327 \\ -\ 52 \\ \hline \end{array}$$

Building the Millions Block
Exploring Patterns and Relationships
in the Number System

What you will *do*:

- Work with a calculator to explore relationships among pairs of numbers from the following list: 1; 10; 100; 1,000; 10,000; 1,000,000.

- Write mathematical statements describing the relationships between those numbers.

- Work together with your classmates to build a model of the millions block, making and revising plans for the model.

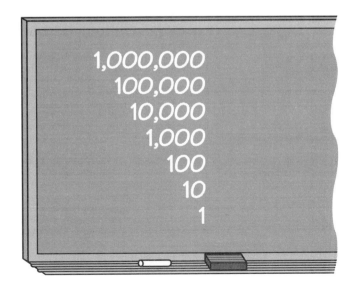

Family Letter

Name _____   Date Due _____

Dear Student,

This week you have been expanding your knowledge of
base-ten numbers to a million and beyond. But how useful
are these really big numbers?

> The Earth is between
> 91,400,000 and
> 94,600,00 miles
> from the Sun.

Home Work

Fun Facts

1. Think of something you're really interested in—stamps,
   baseball, astronomy, movies, ballet, whales, whatever.

2. Find a favorite number fact related to your topic. Fill in
   the fact on the appropriate line below. Can you find a
   fact for every line?

3. When your fact sheet is complete, bring it back to school
   to share with the class.

1	_____
10	_____
100	_____
1,000	_____
10,000	_____
100,000	_____
1,000,000	_____
Beyond	_____

Name _____   Date _____

1. Shade $\frac{5}{8}$ of this circle.

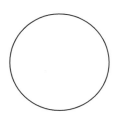

2. Circle the polygon that does not belong. Tell why you think so.

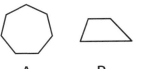

   A   B   C

3. If a $\frac{1}{3}$ fraction piece were covered with 4 pieces, all the same size, what would

    those pieces be? _____

4. If you multiply this number by 3 and subtract 7 you get 17.

    What is the number? _____

5. How many centimeters are there in $2\frac{1}{4}$ meters? _____

6. Write the fraction that names the shaded part. _____

7. How is 104,030 read?

    A   ten thousand, four hundred thirty

    B   one hundred four thousand, thirty

    C   ten thousand four thousand, thirty

    D   one hundred forty thousand, thirty

8. Write two numbers that the answer falls between.

$$47 + 239 = \boxed{} \qquad \rule{2cm}{0.4pt} \qquad \rule{2cm}{0.4pt}$$

9. Write the missing number.

    61, 49, 37, _____, 13

10. In the circles, write the signs that make the equation true.

    (6 $\bigcirc$ 3) $\bigcirc$ 3 = 9

Birdseed by the Million
Using Estimation Techniques to Count 1 Million

What you will do:

- Predict whether a bag of birdseed contains one million seeds.

- Devise a plan for checking your predictions and report to the class.

- Help to display the class' plan that shows what one million bird seeds would look like.

- Take what you learned from the experience with bird seeds and apply it to finding what one million of other objects would look like.

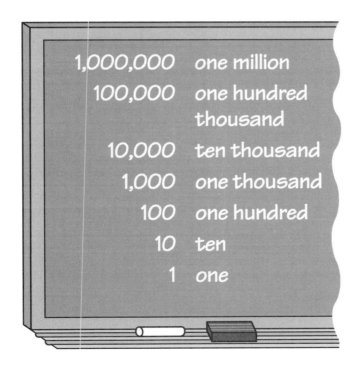

1,000,000	one million
100,000	one hundred thousand
10,000	ten thousand
1,000	one thousand
100	one hundred
10	ten
1	one

MathLand® Student Resource Book • Grade 5—23511
© Creative Publications

Name _____   Date Due _____

Dear Student,

This week we've been investigating a million. You may have been surprised by how large a million really is. Now here's a real challenge.

Home Work

I Spy a Million!

1. Find a million of something in your house, yard, or neighborhood.

2. You don't need to bring your million to class. Just describe what it is, how big it is, how you know it's about a million, and where it's found.

About Your Week

Millions Equations
Using Estimation and Calculation Techniques
with Large Numbers

What you will do:

Day Trip One:
- Use a variety of numbers and operation signs to discover how many different ways there are to name a million.

Day Trip Two:
- Try to come up with 6 numbers, from 1 to 6 digits, whose sum comes as close to one million, without going over.

Day Trip Three:
- Discover patterns in large multiplication problems and predict the number of digits in the answers.

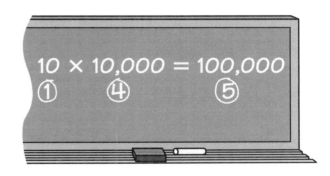

Day Trip Four:
- Solve a prepared maze and find the path to 1,000,000.

- Add numbers and operations to create your own maze in which one path leads to 1,000,000. Exchange papers with a partner and try to solve each other's mazes.

Day Trip Five:
- Play a "Million Guesstimation" game with a partner by trying to find the best number to complete a problem.

Family Letter

Name _____   Date Due _____

Dear Student,

This week we have been working with millions equations. You created a one-million maze at school and solved another. Now it's time to a-MAZE your family.

Home Work

A-Maze-ing Million

1. Use the outline to create a million maze. Keep a record of the right route.

2. Add numbers to the false pathways as distractions.

3. Give it to someone in your family to solve.

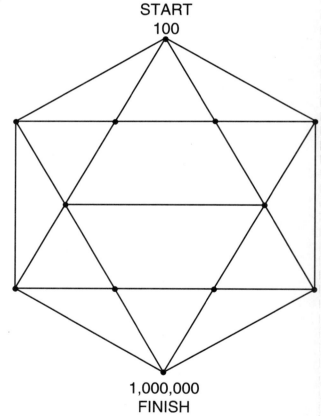

START
100

1,000,000
FINISH

Please note: For an upcoming math project, we will need clean, empty milk containers: small (from cafeteria), pint, quart, half gallon, and gallon. We will also need rinsed and dried drink containers of different sizes. Note the cost of the beverage and if possible mark with a marker or masking tape the level to which the container was filled. Don't bring in any glass!

Sample Maze

Name _____

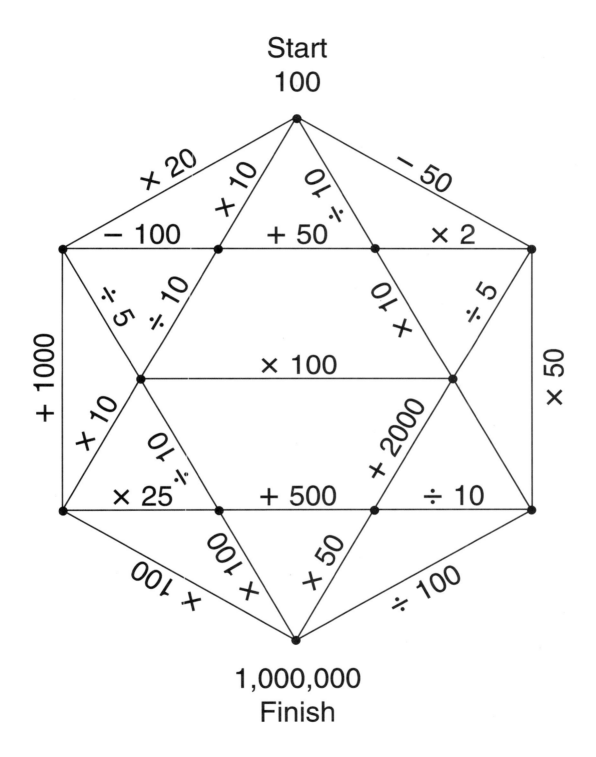

Start
100

× 20

× 10

÷ 10

− 50

− 100

+ 50

× 2

÷ 5

÷ 10

× 10

÷ 5

+ 1000

× 100

× 50

× 10

÷ 10

+ 2000

× 25

+ 500

÷ 10

× 100

× 100

× 50

÷ 100

1,000,000
Finish

MathLand® Student Resource Book • Grade 5—23511
© Creative Publications

Blank Maze

Name _____

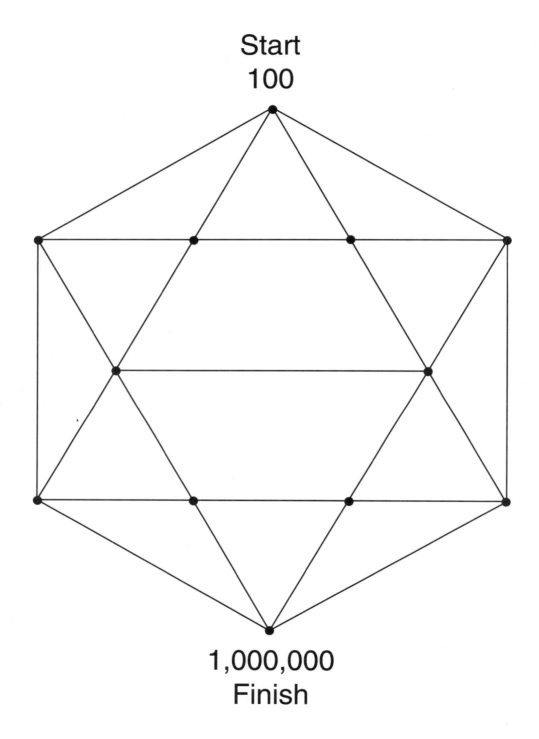

Start
100

1,000,000
Finish

Million Guesstimation

You Will Need
- 2 players
- paper
- pencils
- 1 calculator

1. The object of the game is to complete a number problem so that the answer is as close to 1,000,000 as you can get.

2. Player A writes down an incomplete problem, such as 789 x _____.

3. Player B guesses and writes down a number to go in the blank, trying to get an answer that is as close to 1,000,000 as possible.

4. Player A uses a calculator to find the answer, and Player B writes the answer down next to her guess. This tells Player B whether her guess is high or low.

5. Player B continues guessing numbers, using feedback and estimation, until she comes as close to 1,000,000 as possible (using whole numbers).

6. Players A and B switch roles and repeat the game.

Millions Questions
Finding Out More About Large Numbers

What you will *do*:

- Debate the question—"How long would it take to count to one million"—and come up with a good strategy to find the answer.

- Come up with your own million questions and answers.

- Select your favorite million questions and answers and place them in a class book. Present the strategies you used in words and pictures to include in the book.

60 seconds	=	1 minute
60 minutes	=	1 hour
24 hours	=	1 day
7 days	=	1 week
52 weeks	=	1 year
365 days	=	1 year

Name _____   Date Due _____

Dear Student,

This week we have been exploring all sorts of questions about a million. Here's a question to explore with your family, "Can you eat a million meals in a lifetime?"

Home Work

Can You Eat a Million Meals in a Lifetime?

1. Record the predictions of various members of your family to the question, "Can you eat a million meals in a lifetime?" Be sure to include your own prediction.

2. Agree on a strategy and find an actual answer.

3. Check your answer against your predictions. Did you know as much or more about a million than your family members?

Please note: For an upcoming math project, we will need clean, empty milk containers: small (from cafeteria), pint, quart, half gallon, and gallon. We will also need rinsed and dried drink containers of different sizes. Note the cost of the beverage and if possible mark with a marker or masking tape the level to which the container was filled. In some cases if the container was part of a package of six, for example, the price will have to be figured out. Do not bring in any glass containers!

Big Number Line

Using Estimation and Number Sense with a Number Line

What you will do:

- Name numbers represented by letters on a number line.

- Create your own number line and place letters on it to represent information of your own choosing.

- Guess which facts are represented by letters on number lines created by your classmates.

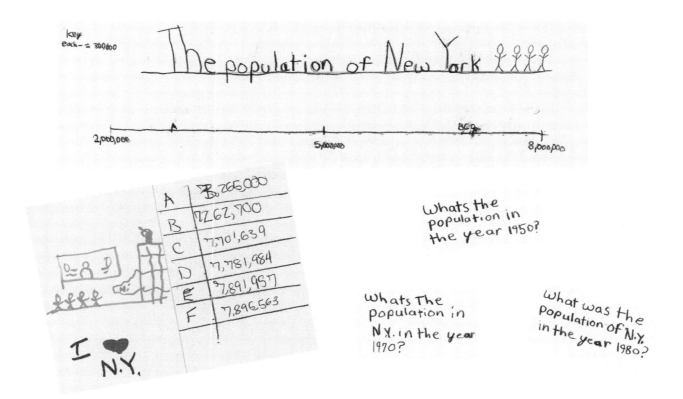

Family Letter

Name _____   Date Due _____

Dear Student,

Throughout this unit you have been exploring a million in many different ways. In the course of our work, you have probably learned a lot about a million and other large numbers. Tell your family some of the things you have learned.

A million is more than 100,000 and less than 1,000,000,000

Home Work

I Didn't Know That!

1. Here are some questions that may help you remember facts you want to tell your family. You can use them to make some notes for your report.

   A. How big is a million?

   B. What does a millions cube look like?

   C. How many thousands are there in a million?

   D. What is another name for a million?

   E. Can you name something you know there are about a million of?

2. Did you surprise your family with some of your facts? Ask one of your family members to use the back of this paper to comment on something surprising or interesting he or she learned.

3. Then bring the paper back to school to share with the class.

Reminder: Soon we'll be starting the math project for which we need the milk and the drink containers. Please be sure you remember to bring them to school.

Name _____   Date _____

1. What number is next?

7, 2, 9, 4, 11, 6, _____

2. Draw a rectangle. Shade it to show $\frac{5}{6}$.

3. Eight blocks are covered. All the blocks show 234. Sketch the covered blocks.

4. What number comes between the two numbers below?

143,089 _____ 143,091

5. What number comes next?

38, 29, 25, 16, 12, _____

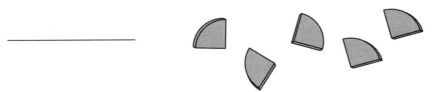
6. Together, are these pieces more than, less than, or equal to one whole?

_____

7. What is $\frac{2}{5}$ of 20? _____

8. In the picture below, 2 third pieces are covered with 8 other pieces.

What fraction is each of the 8 pieces? _____

9. Write the fraction that tells what part of the cubes is white. _____

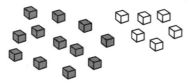

10. How is 370,206 read?

   A   three hundred seventy-two thousand, six

   B   thirty-seven thousand, two hundred six

   C   three hundred seventy thousand, two hundred six

Name _____   Date _____

Solve each problem.

1. How many 10s are there in 1,000,000? _____

2. How many 100s are there in 10,000? _____

Circle T if the equation is true. Circle F if the equation is false.

3. $100 \times 100 \times 100 = 1,000,000$ T   F

4. $1,000 \times 10,000 \times 100 = 10,000,000$ T   F

5. $10,000 \times 100 = 1,000,000$ T   F

How many boxes or bags would it take to have 1,000,000 of each item?

6. Number of raisins in a box = 1,000. Number of boxes needed = _____

7. Number of candies in a bag = 500. Number of bags needed = _____

8. Grains of birdseed in a box = 25,000. Number of boxes needed = _____

Q44 MathLand® Student Resource Book • Grade 5—23511
© Creative Publications

9. Find a path from start to finish in which the numbers and operations get you to 1,000,000. Show the calculations you did to prove your path works.

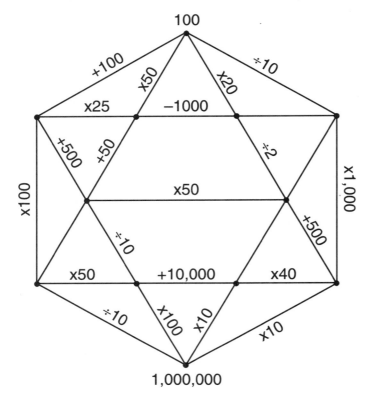

10. Suppose 200 people jump out of airplanes every hour (wearing parachutes, that is). At this rate, how many hours would it take for 1,000,000 people to jump out of airplanes? How many days is that? How many weeks is that? About how many months is that? Show your calculations on a separate sheet of paper. Estimate where appropriate.

Write the value of each letter on the blanks underneath the number lines. Some answers may require estimates.

11.

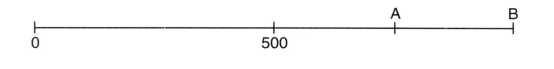

12.

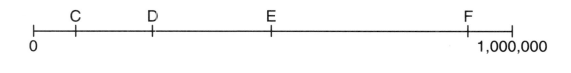

13.

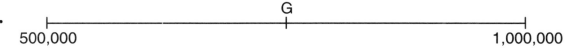

Name _____

Box Builders
Exploring Volume of Rectangular Solids

What you will do:

• Use Rainbow Cubes to build boxes called rectangular solids. Find the dimensions and volume of the rectangular solids that you build.

• Find the missing dimensions in Mystery Solids problems.

• Explore rectangular solids of different dimensions to discover the special relationship: length times width times height equals volume.

• Use grid paper models to build the largest box possible beginning with a 20 cm x 20 cm sheet of grid paper.

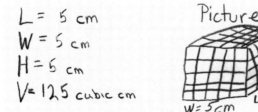

L = 5 cm
W = 5 cm
H = 5 cm
V = 125 cubic cm

Picture

H = 5cm
L = 5cm
W = 5cm

How I found the volume was that
I multiplied the length times width and it
equals twenty-five. Then I multiplied
twenty-five times the height and that equals
one hundred twenty-five, and that is the volume
of the rectangular solid.

Name _____   Date Due _____

Dear Student,

This week you have been exploring boxes and their volumes. Volume is the measure of what a container holds. You have learned how to find the volume of a box, how to find one dimension of the box if you know the other two dimensions, and how to work with decimals.

Home Work

Is It Bigger or Smaller?

Now you'll investigate some boxes at home.

1. Find five boxes.

2. Use the centimeter ruler on this sheet to measure each of them.

3. Draw a model of each box and record its dimensions.

4. Make a prediction about which box will have the greatest volume.

5. Use a calculator at school to find all the volumes and see if your prediction was correct.

Reminder: It's time to bring in the clean, empty milk containers you've been collecting. We'll be using them next week.

20 × 20 cm Grid

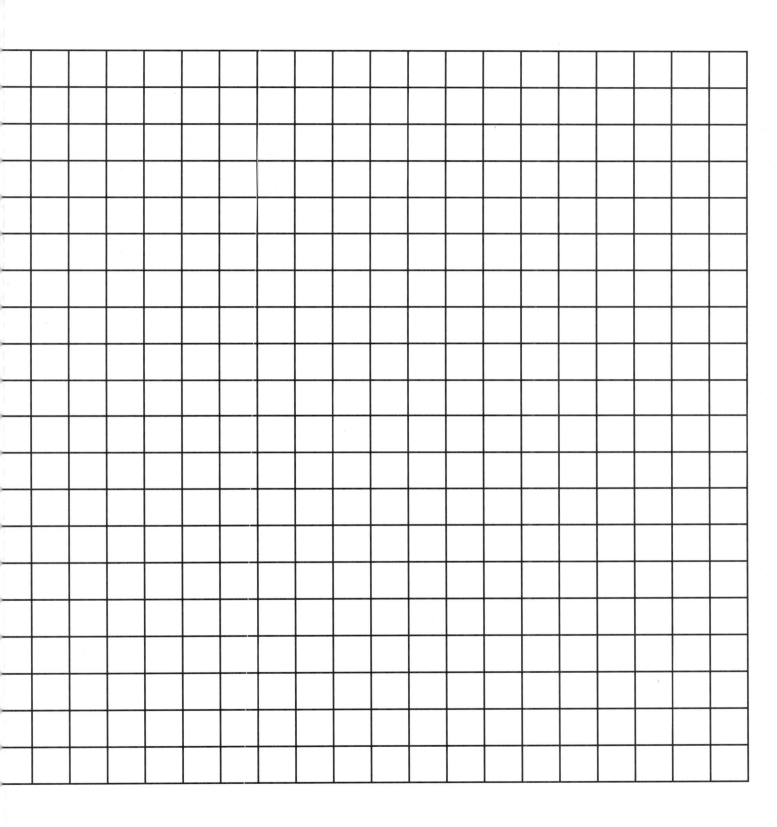

20 × 20 cm Grid

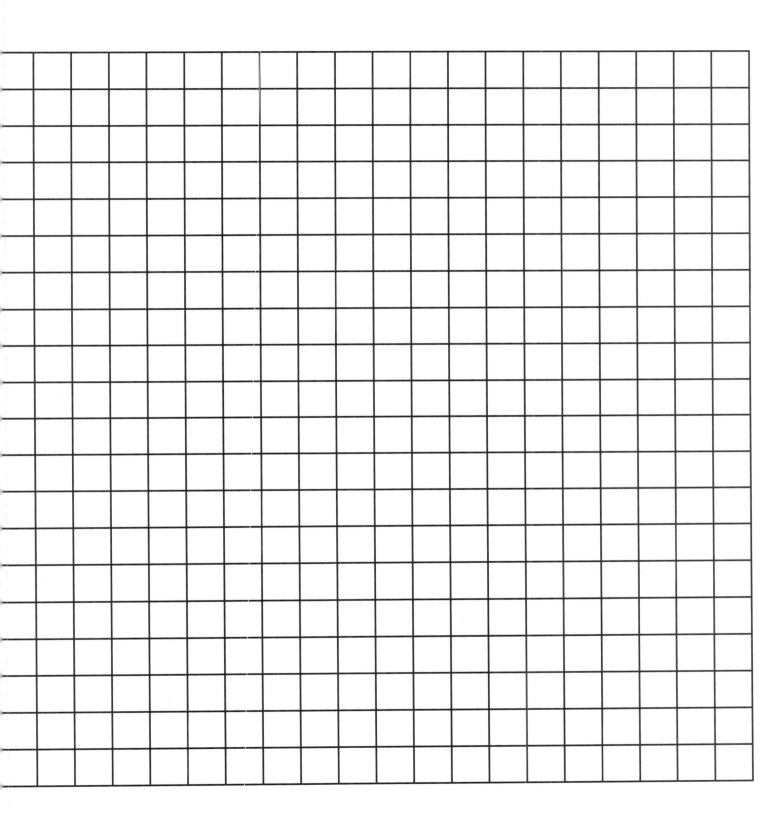

Rectangular Solids Explorations

1. Use your blocks to build these rectangular solids:

    4 cm × 3 cm × 5 cm
    5 cm × 5 cm × 5 cm
    2 cm × 5 cm × 1.1 cm
    2 cm × 2 cm × 1.5 cm
    3 cm × 5 cm × 1.2 cm
    2 cm × 3 cm × 2.2 cm

    Draw sketches of each solid and label its dimensions. What is the volume of each? Verify the volume with your calculator. Does it agree?

2. Here are some mystery solids:

    Volume: 24 cm³; length: 2 cm; width: 6 cm; height: ?
    Volume: 9 cm³; length: 2 cm; width: 3 cm; height: ?
    Volume: 12 cm³; length: 2 cm; width: 5 cm; height: ?
    Volume: 15 cm³; length: 2 cm; width: 3 cm; height: ?

    Draw sketches of each solid and label its dimensions. Verify with your calculator. Does it agree?

3. How many different rectangular solids having a volume of 36 cm³ can you make? Draw sketches of each solid and label its dimensions.

20 × 20 cm Grid

20 × 20 cm Grid

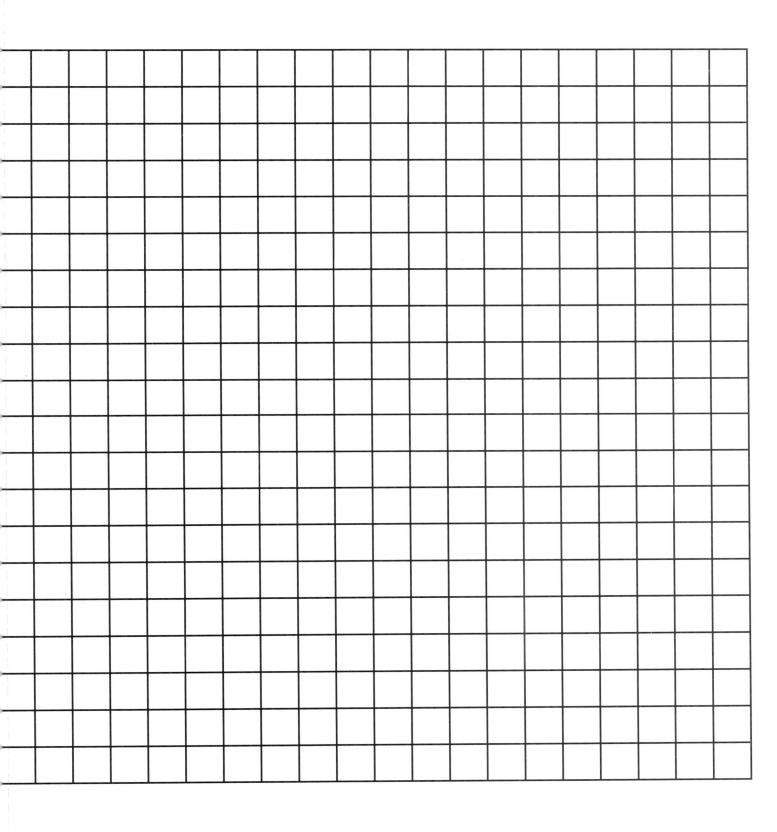

Creating Containers
Investigating Capacity and Liquid Measure

What you will do:

- Make a chart showing the relationships among different units of liquid measure.

- Make your own measuring sets for measuring liquids.

- Use your measuring sets to prepare an imaginary fruit punch.

Tropical Punch

2 1/4 C orange juice
6 oz. mango juice
46 oz. pineapple juice
1.5 qt. soda water
1/4 C. grenadine syrup

46	46	46	#oz. 120
6	6	6	6 oz. surving 120
18	18	18	
+ 2	32	32	The way we made the
62	+ 6	16	Tropical Punch is to first
	118	+ 2	translate all measure-
		120	ments to oz. Then all the

The way we made the Tropical Punch is to first translate all measurements to oz. Then all the oz. up. That is how we measured the recipe.

Family Letter

Name _____   Date Due _____

Dear Student,

This week you have been making your own set of
measurement tools to measure capacity. Capacity is
how much a container will hold. You learned about
the relationships among ounces, cups, pints, quarts,
and gallons. Then you used your tools to solve a
real-life problem.

From the kitchen of: _____

Ingredients:

Home Work

My Favorite Recipe

Let's see what you can cook up at home.

1. Find a favorite recipe that includes at
   least two ingredients that are in units
   of liquid measure.

2. Pretend you have a measuring set that
   is calibrated only in ounces.

3. Rewrite the recipe, converting all the
   units of liquid measure to ounces.

4. Would the recipe be easier to make if
   it were written all in ounces or the
   way it was originally written?
   Tell why.

Reminder: It's time to bring in the drink containers you've been
collecting. We'll be using them in class next week. Remember, each
container should be marked to show the level of the liquid when the
container was full.

Liquid Measurement

4 cups	32 oz	1 quart
$3\frac{1}{2}$ cups	28 oz	
3 cups	24 oz	
$2\frac{1}{2}$ cups	20 oz	
2 cups	16 oz	1 pint
$1\frac{1}{2}$ cups	12 oz	
1 cup	8 oz	
$\frac{1}{2}$ cup	4 oz	

Name _____

Looking Back

Tropical Punch

Try out your measuring sets to mix a batch of imaginary punch.
Here's the recipe:

Tropical Punch

$2\frac{1}{4}$ c orange juice

46 oz pineapple juice

6 oz mango juice

$\frac{1}{4}$ c grenadine syrup

$1\frac{1}{2}$ qt soda water

Amount of punch:

Number of 6-oz servings:

More or Less
Analyzing Capacity and Price Per Ounce

What you will do:

- Figure out a method for determining price per ounce.

- Use your own measuring sets to find out the capacity of different containers. Determine the price per ounce of different drinks.

- Organize your information into a written format.

- Use your measuring sets and knowledge of drink containers to find the best buy for a class party.

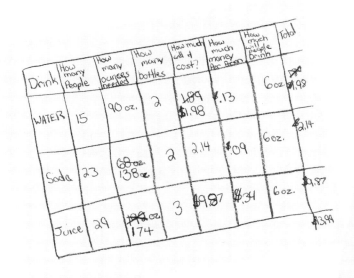

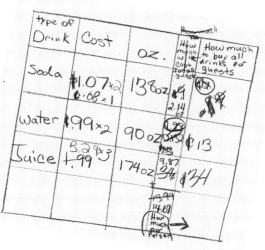

Name _____   Date Due _____

Dear Student,

This week you used your measuring sets and what you learned about measuring volume to find the capacities and the prices per ounce of the drink containers you brought from home. Just as last week, you ended the week by solving a real-world problem. This week's homework involves a different real-world experiment.

Home Work

How Much Is That Drink?

1. Go on a field trip to the grocery store with someone in your family. Find your favorite drink.

2. Read the labels for all the different sizes of the drink.

3. Record what you see on the labels and the price of each size.

4. When you come back to school, use your calculator to figure out which size is the best buy.

5. Think about things other than price per ounce that you might want to consider when buying a product. Make some notes about your thoughts so that you can discuss them in class.

Name of Drink: _____

Size of Container	Price Per Ounce
_____	_____
_____	_____
_____	_____
_____	_____
_____	_____

Products

- Brand A liquid dish soap holds 42 fl oz and costs $2.89.

- For $1.59, you get 22 fl oz of Brand B dish soap.

- The Big Apple Market has a special on Brand C soap, 32 fl oz for $1.35.

- Brand D soap is 40 fl oz for $1.79.

- The 8.5 fl oz size of Brand A olive oil sells for $2.19.

- Brand B olive oil is $3.45 for 17 fl oz.

- The Big Apple also has Brand C olive oil on sale. It is $5.45 for 34 fl oz.

- The 12 fl oz size of Brand D olive oil is $2.25.

Products

Container #	Type of Drink	Price	Capacity	Price per ounce
1				
2				
3				
4				
5				
6				
7				
8				
9				
10				

Name _____   Date _____

1. What is the volume of a rectangular solid that is

3.2 cm × 6 cm × 5 cm? _____

2. A rectangular solid has a volume of 168 cm³. Its length is 4 cm, and its height is 7 cm. On a separate sheet of paper, sketch this solid and label its three dimensions.

A company produces a product called Tree Tea which comes in boxes that measure 3 inches by 3 inches by 3 inches. Design a carton to hold 24 boxes of Tree Tea.

3. One possible carton has a width of 18 inches and a length of 6 inches.

What is the carton's height? _____

4. What are the dimensions of two other cartons that could be used to hold exactly 24 boxes?

Name _____

Emilio wants to make fruit punch. Here is the recipe he uses.

$2\frac{1}{4}$ cups orange juice	24 ounces pineapple juice
4 ounces mango juice	$1\frac{1}{2}$ quarts soda water
$\frac{1}{4}$ cup grenadine syrup	

Solve the following problems. You may refer to the Equivalent Measures Chart that you made in class.

6. How much punch will the recipe make? _____

7. How many 6-ounce servings will the recipe make? _____

8. Emilio needs to buy pineapple juice.
Brand A holds 32 ounces and costs $3.45.
Brand B holds 40 ounces and costs $3.85.
Which is a better buy? Explain your answer in writing.

Name _____

Fraction Experts
Exploring Equivalent Fractions with Fraction Circles

What you will *do*:

- Label and expand your Fraction Circle sets.

- Create an Equivalent Fractions Chart.

- Look for patterns among equivalent fractions. Record your findings on the fractions chart.

- Use the information you have gathered about fractions to complete the chart.

- Use the patterns you have discovered to extend the fraction chart.

Can you make	with wholes	with halves	with thirds	with fourths	with fifths	with sixths	with sevenths	with eighths	with ninths	with tenths	with elevenths	with twelfths
1	1											
$\frac{1}{2}$		$\frac{1}{2}$		$\frac{2}{4}$		$\frac{3}{6}$		$\frac{4}{8}$		$\frac{5}{10}$		$\frac{6}{12}$
$\frac{1}{3}$			$\frac{1}{3}$			$\frac{2}{6}$			$\frac{3}{9}$			$\frac{4}{12}$
$\frac{1}{4}$				$\frac{1}{4}$				$\frac{2}{8}$				$\frac{3}{12}$
$\frac{1}{5}$					$\frac{1}{5}$					$\frac{2}{10}$		
$\frac{1}{6}$						$\frac{1}{6}$						$\frac{2}{12}$
$\frac{1}{7}$							$\frac{1}{7}$					
$\frac{1}{8}$								$\frac{1}{8}$				
$\frac{1}{9}$									$\frac{1}{9}$			

Family Letter

Name _____   Date Due _____

Dear Student,

This week you've begun a unit on fractions. You've used your Fraction Circles to explore equivalent fractions. (Equivalent fractions have different names but are equal in value.) For example, $\frac{1}{2}$ and $\frac{2}{4}$ are equivalent fractions. You have contributed to the class Equivalent Fractions Chart. The patterns found in the chart are helpful for writing other equivalent fractions.

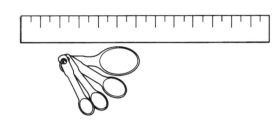

Home Work

Fractions Scavenger Hunt

1. Fractions are all around us! Look around your house for fractions. Cookbooks, newspapers, magazines, and tools used for measuring are some common household items that often involve fractions.

2. Note the fraction numerals and where you found the fraction. We will add your findings to a class graph and see if we can determine the most common fractions and the most common uses of fractions.

Name _____   Date _____

1. How is 4,370,593 read?

    A   four million, thirty-seven thousand, five hundred ninety-three

    B   four million, three hundred seventy thousand, five hundred ninety-three

    C   four hundred thirty-seven thousand, five hundred ninety-three

2. There are 7 groups of 6 people on a ferris wheel, and one group of 4.

    How many people are there altogether? _____

3. Write the fraction that tells what part of the cubes is shaded. _____

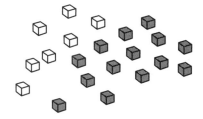

4. Write the rule for changing the first number to the second.

    $8 \rightarrow 4,$ $5 \rightarrow 1,$ $10 \rightarrow 6$ _____

5. Write signs in the circles to make a correct equation.

    $(18 \bigcirc 2) \bigcirc 4 = 5$

6. Draw ones blocks in the shape of a rectangle to show 3 x 8.

7. Write the next number.

490,948   490,949   _____

8. Write 2 numbers that the answer falls between.

$803 - 659 =$ ☐   _____   _____

9. Write the missing number.

1, 4, 9, _____, 25, 36

10. Which of these is an improper fraction?

A $\frac{2}{3}$

B $\frac{7}{12}$

C $\frac{1}{3}$

D $\frac{3}{2}$

MathLand® Student Resource Book • Grade 5—23511
© Creative Publications

About "About"
Defining and Naming Fractional Parts of Sets

What you will *do*:

- Write multiplication and division equations to describe the same fractional part of a set.

- Work with a partner to make up story problems involving fractional parts of sets of objects around the room.

- Exchange the problems you and your partner made up with another pair of classmates. Solve each other's problems.

- Present the problems you solved to the rest of the class.

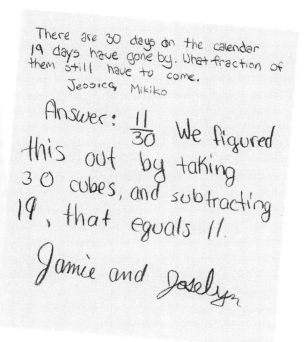

Name _____   Date Due _____

Dear Student,

This week you and your partner have been making up fraction problems about sets of things in the classroom for your classmates to solve. Are there sets of things around your home?

Home Work

What fraction of the wheels belongs to cars?

Fraction Questions

1. Look for groups of things at home to write fraction questions about.

2. Write down two or three problems to bring to school.

3. Share your problems with the class at the end of the week.

Approaching Accuracy
Comparing and Ordering Fractional Numbers

What you will *do*:

- Use number cards to construct fractional numbers.

- Place each fraction on a number line by using your knowledge of equivalent fractions or by making sketches.

- Use fraction cards to set up addition sentences. Compare the two sides of each sentence and choose from the symbols for greater than, less than, about, and equal, to make a true mathematical sentence.

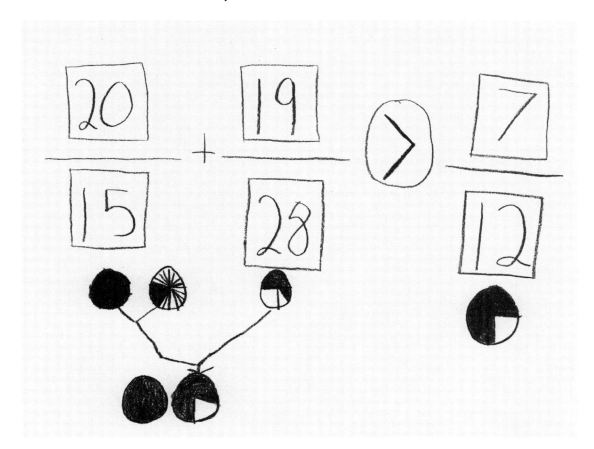

Name _____   Date Due _____

Dear Student,

This week we have been making a variety of fractions and have been trying to place them on our number lines. Some of them are easy to place. Others are pretty difficult, but we can use our Fraction Circles to help us. Let's see if you can place some fractions without using your fraction pieces.

Home Work

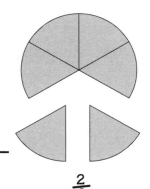

$\frac{2}{6}$

On the Line

Look at the fractions below. Place each one on the number line as accurately as you can.

$$\frac{14}{5} \qquad \frac{2}{6} \qquad \frac{12}{8} \qquad \frac{16}{15}$$

$$\frac{8}{12} \qquad \frac{201}{100} \qquad \frac{18}{9}$$

0   1   2   3

Try These Today...

Name _____

1.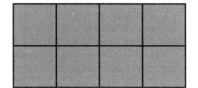

2.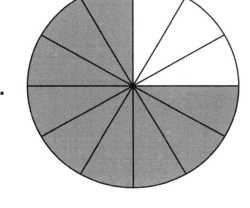

3.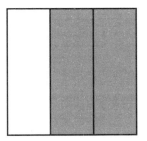

MathLand® Student Resource Book • Grade 5—23511
© Creative Publications

On the Line

You Will Need
- 2 players
- Fraction Circles
- 60 number cards (2 cards for each of the numbers 1–30)
- 11" x 17" paper
- pencils

1. Partners draw a 0–3 number line on the paper.

2. Partners shuffle the cards and place them face down.

3. Each partner draws a number card. The partners use the two cards to show a fraction they can place on their number line.

4. Partners estimate where on the number line the fraction will go and test their estimate using Fraction Circles or by making sketches.

5. Partners write their fraction on the number line and sketch a picture to show why that placement is correct.

6. Partners draw two new number cards and repeat steps 2–4.

Boxes in Boxes
Applying Fraction Concepts and Measurement in Three Dimensions

What you will do:

- Measure the dimensions of various school supply objects.

- Determine how many school supplies can be packed into each of 3 shipping box sizes.

- Find the lowest-cost shipping method for large orders of school supplies.

	small	Medium	Large
Markers	7	9	32
crayons	9	13	48
Paper	0	0	7
Dictionary	0	0	5
Paper clips	32	56	136
Staples	15	36	108
Tape	36	48	204
Kleenex	0	0	5

Family Letter

Name _____   Date Due _____

Dear Student,

This week you have been measuring, calculating, estimating, and sketching to decide how many small items you could fit in various sizes of shipping boxes. Here's a problem for you to solve at home. It's about fitting furniture into a bedroom.

Home Work

Furniture Floor Plans

Imagine that you are moving to a new home and that your new bedroom will have the shape and size shown below. You want to plan the arrangement of your bedroom furniture before moving in.

1. How would you place the furniture?

2. Make a sketch of your favorite arrangement.

3. Include the dimensions of each object to prove that your arrangement would fit.

Your Furniture
Bed: $6\frac{1}{2}$ feet long, $3\frac{1}{2}$ feet wide
Dresser: $2\frac{1}{2}$ feet long, $1\frac{1}{2}$ feet deep
Desk: 4 feet long, 2 feet wide
Chair: $1\frac{1}{2}$ feet long, $1\frac{1}{2}$ feet wide
Rug: 6 feet long, $3\frac{1}{2}$ feet wide

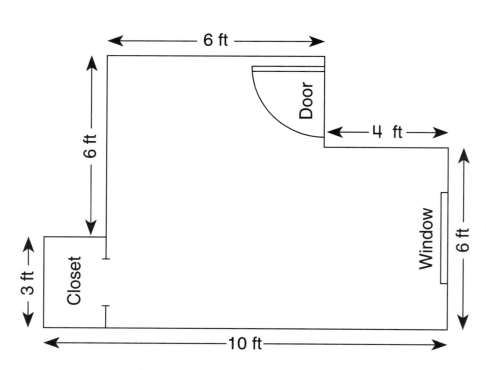

Quiz Makers
Creating and Solving Money Problems

What you will do:

Day Trip One:
*   Use mental math and calculation to find out how many nickels are in $10.00. Make up your own "How many" questions in a multiple-choice quiz format.

Day Trip Two:
*   Find the price of grapes per pound to determine if you have enough money to buy 5 pounds worth.

Day Trip Three:
*   Find five different ways to make change for $10.00 using only nickels and dimes.

Day Trip Four:
*   Add up fractional parts of whole dollars to solve the problem of the day.

Day Trip Five:
*   Take the quizzes you've been making all week and exchange them with a partner. Take each other's quizzes.

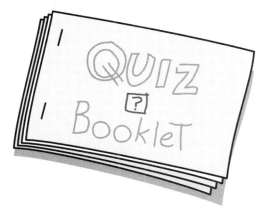

Name _____

Dear Student,

This week you have been working with your partner to make up questions about money and to write multiple-choice answers for them. At the end of the week, you'll exchange the quiz books you've written with other classmates and take each other's quizzes. Here's a chance to make up a quiz for a member of your family to solve.

How many nickels are in $10.00?

a) 100

b) 200

c) 20

d) more than a. and b. put together?

Home Work

Quiz Masters

1. Make up several problems about money.

2. Write at least four multiple-choice solutions to each problem.

3. Find a family member who will take your quiz.

4. Check the answers.

5. How did that person do?

Problems of the Day

Day Trip One
How many nickels are in $10.00?
- a) 100
- b) 200
- c) 20
- d) more than a) and b) put together

Day Trip Two
You have $6.50 with which to buy 5 pounds of grapes for a big party. Grapes cost $1.40 per pound. Will you have enough money?
- a) Yes, with 50¢ left over.
- b) No. You need $32.50.
- c) No. You need 50¢ more.
- d) Yes. You have exactly enough.

Day Trip Three
Which of the following describes a correct way to make change for $10.00 using only nickels and dimes?
- a) 100 nickels and 50 dimes
- b) 50 nickels and 100 dimes
- c) 20 nickels and 90 dimes
- d) none of the above
- e) both a) and b)
- f) both a) and c)

Day Trip Four
I spent $\frac{1}{2}$ of a dollar, $\frac{1}{5}$ of a dollar, $\frac{2}{10}$ of a dollar, and $\frac{3}{4}$ of a dollar. How much did I spend all together?
- a) $1.65
- b) 90¢
- c) $1.55
- d) $1.45
- e) None of the above. Write in the correct answer.

Name _____   Date _____

1. About what fraction of these cubes is shaded? _____

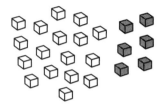

2. What is $\frac{5}{6}$ of 18? _____

3. Write an addition equation using these eighth pieces. _____

4. Write two numbers that the answer is between.

$7 \times 67 =$ ☐   _____   _____

5. Write two numbers that the answer is between.

$453 + 137 =$ ☐   _____   _____

6. Write the number that comes before 50,370. _____

7. Write a multiplication equation that the fraction pieces show.

_____

8. Write the rule for changing the first number to the second.

$4 \rightarrow 14,$ $7 \rightarrow 23,$ $2 \rightarrow 8$ _____

9. Circle the greatest number.

61,111   60,899   60,911   600,001

10. Write the multiplication equation that the blocks show.

_____

MathLand® Student Resource Book • Grade 5—23511
© Creative Publications

Name _____   Date _____

1. Write at least 5 equivalent fractions for $\frac{2}{3}$. Explain how you know they are equivalent.

2. Use cubes to solve this problem: What is $\frac{1}{4}$ of 17?
   Sketch how you used the cubes to solve the problem.

3. Write equations to go with the sketch you drew above.

   Multiplication equation: _____

   Division equation: _____

4. There are 26 counties in Wyoming. Interstate Route 80 passes through 6 counties. Through about what fraction of the of counties does Interstate Route 80 pass? On another sheet of paper, explain your answer.

Use the circle graphs to answer problems 5–9. Circle T if the statement is true. Circle F if the statement is false.

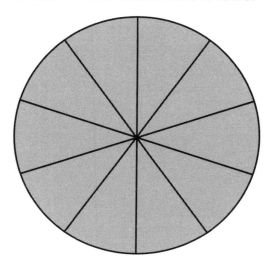 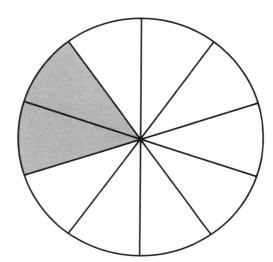

5. The shaded part of the two circles equals $1\frac{1}{5}$.   T   F

6. The shaded part of the two circles is between $1\frac{1}{2}$ and 2.   T   F

7. The shaded part of the two circles equals $\frac{6}{5}$.   T   F

8. The shaded part of the two circles is $> \frac{4}{3}$.   T   F

9. The shaded part of the two circles is $< \frac{14}{10}$.   T   F

Name _____

10. $\frac{17}{6}$ $\frac{3}{9}$ $\frac{15}{7}$ $\frac{18}{12}$ $\frac{251}{100}$

Place each of these 5 fractions on the number line. Estimate as closely as you can.

0   1   2   3

11. Write the correct symbol ($<$, $>$, or $=$) to complete this statement:

$\frac{1}{8} + \frac{6}{5}$ _____ $\frac{7}{8}$

In the space below, use words, pictures, or numbers to prove your answer.

12. June spent $\frac{1}{4}$ of a dollar, $\frac{2}{5}$ of a dollar, $\frac{7}{10}$ of a dollar, and $\frac{1}{2}$ of a dollar. How much did she spend in all?

○ $1.00   ○ $1.85   ○ $1.75   ○ $2.00

Name _____   Date _____

Solve these problems as quickly as you can. Use the strategies that work best for you.

1. $195 \div 15 =$ _____

2. $1000 \times 100 =$ _____

3. $\frac{3}{4}$ of $100 =$ _____

4. $1000 \div 10 =$ _____

5. $\$2.88 \div 32 =$ _____

6. $25{,}000 \times 40 =$ _____

7. $\frac{6}{10}$ of $100 =$ _____

8. $4673 + 2127 =$ _____

9. $10^3 =$ _____

10. $7\overline{)53}$

11. $\frac{3}{5} + \frac{3}{10} =$ _____

12. $3^3 =$ _____

13. $67 \times 4 =$ _____

14. $\frac{1}{4} \times 24 =$ _____

15.
$$\begin{array}{r} 315 \\ -\ 191 \\ \hline \end{array}$$

16.
$$\begin{array}{r} \frac{7}{9} \\ -\ \frac{4}{9} \\ \hline \end{array}$$

17.
$$\begin{array}{r} \$8.72 \\ \times\ \ \ 12 \\ \hline \end{array}$$

18.
$$\begin{array}{r} \frac{5}{6} \\ +\ 1\frac{1}{3} \\ \hline \end{array}$$

19.
$$\begin{array}{r} 3910 \\ 147 \\ +\ \ \ 29 \\ \hline \end{array}$$

20.
$$\begin{array}{r} \$1003.23 \\ -\ \ \ 163.09 \\ \hline \end{array}$$

MathLand® Student Resource Book • Grade 5—23511
© Creative Publications

What's Your Angle?
Exploring Angles of Polygons

What you will do:

- Use Fraction Circle pieces to make your own protractors.

- Use your protractors to measure the angles of a variety of polygons and look for the relationships between the sums of the angles.

- Use what you've learned about angle measurements to determine the measurements of the angles of Pattern Blocks without using protractors.

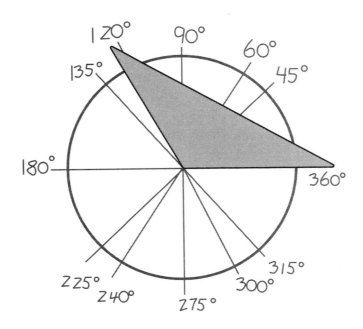

Name _____

Date Due _____

Dear Student,

This week you made your own protractor. You have been using it and a plastic protractor to explore and compare the angle measurements of a variety of polygons.

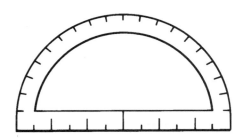

Home Work

Angles, More or Less

Angles are all around us. As you start thinking about angles and looking for them, you'll be amazed at how many you see. Outside class this week look for and trace the following types of angles.

1. Find and trace six 90° angles.

2. Find and trace two angles that are smaller than 90°. These are called *acute* angles.

3. Find and trace two angles that are larger than 90°. These are called *obtuse* angles.

4. Label your angles, telling what object you traced. Write a paragraph about the most common types of angles. Tell why you think they are the most common.

Polygons and Angle Measures

1. Measure the inside angles of a polygon. Record the measurement of each angle. Then find the sum of all the angle measures of that shape.

2. Repeat for other shapes. Start making a chart on which you record your findings. Try to organize the chart in a way that helps you think about the following questions:

   A. What can you say about the sum of the angles of any triangle?

   B. What can you say about the sum of the angles of any quadrilateral?

   C. What about the sums of the angles of polygons with 5, 6, 7, and 8 sides?

   D. Compare your results for different-sided polygons. What can you say about them?

Pattern Block Angles

- Work with your partner to figure out the measurement of each angle of each different Pattern Block shape.

- Trace each shape and record the angle measurements.

- Write down whether each angle is right, acute, or obtuse.

- Write a few sentences about how you figured out the angle measurements.

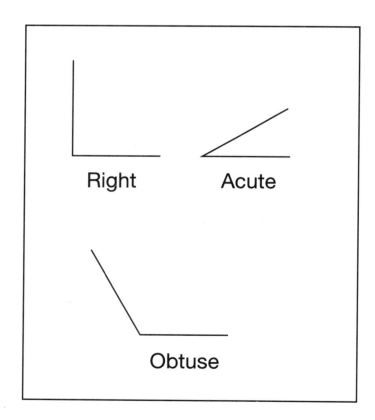

Triangle Trivia
Exploring Sides and Angles of Triangles

What you will do:

- Explore relationships between side lengths of triangles.

- Make different triangles on geoboards and by tracing Polygon Tiles.

- Classify and name each triangle according to their sides and angles. Fill in a class chart on triangles.

- Show off your knowledge of triangles by playing the Triangle Trivia game.

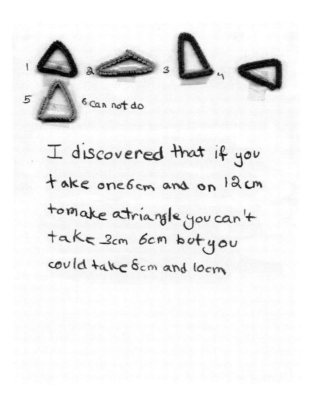

Name _____

Date Due _____

Dear Student,

This week you have continued your study of angles by taking a closer look at a particular polygon with three angles: the triangle. You are exploring relationships of triangle sides and are naming and classifying triangles.

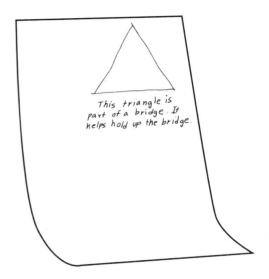

This triangle is part of a bridge. It helps hold up the bridge.

Home Work

Triangle Hunt

This week your homework will be a hunt for triangles. Your goal is to find ten different triangles.

1. Trace or sketch each triangle, trying to keep the side lengths and angles in proportion.

2. Next to each triangle, write the location in which it was found.

3. Write what purpose the triangle serves.

Geoboard Dot Paper

MathLand® Student Resource Book • Grade 5—23511
© Creative Publications

Geoboard Dot Paper

MathLand® Student Resource Book • Grade 5—23511
© Creative Publications

True or False?

1. All of the sides of a triangle can be equal lengths.

2. All of the sides of a triangle can be different lengths.

3. Two of the sides of a triangle can be equal lengths while the third side is a different length.

4. Any three side lengths can form a triangle.

5. Given three side lengths, three different triangles can be made.

6. Given two sides—one 6 cm and the other 12 cm—a triangle can be formed using any one of the following line lengths: 3 cm, 6 cm, 8 cm, 10 cm, 15 cm, and 20 cm.

Triangles

Right Triangle

A triangle with one 90° angle

Obtuse Triangle

A triangle with one angle greater than 90°

Acute Triangle

A triangle with one angle less than 90°

Scalene Triangle

A triangle with all side lengths different

Isosceles Triangle

A triangle with at least two side lengths equal

Equilateral Triangle

A triangle with all side lengths equal

Triangle Trivia

You Will Need
- several teams with 4 players on each team
- team questions about triangles

1. A player from team 1 reads one of the team's questions. The other teams discuss the question and write their response.

2. Each team with the correct answer scores one point. If no team has the correct answer, the team that wrote the question scores a point.

3. Play continues with each team in turn reading one question.

4. The winner is the team with the most points at the end of math time.

Shaping Tessellations
Investigating Polygons that Tessellate

What you will do:

- Sort and classify Polygon Tiles according to their sides and their angles.

- Find Polygon Tiles that will tessellate.

- Make predictions about which polygon shapes will tessellate around a point.

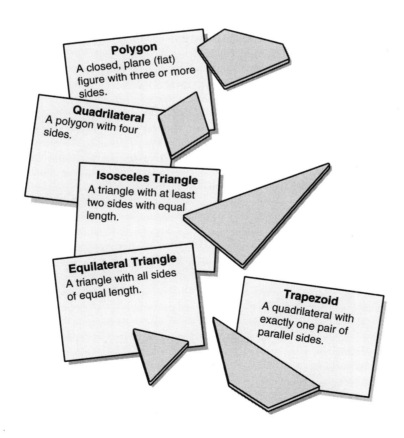

Polygon
A closed, plane (flat) figure with three or more sides.

Quadrilateral
A polygon with four sides.

Isosceles Triangle
A triangle with at least two sides with equal length.

Equilateral Triangle
A triangle with all sides of equal length.

Trapezoid
A quadrilateral with exactly one pair of parallel sides.

Family Letter

Name _____

Dear Student,

This week you are continuing your exploration of angles as you look at shapes that will tessellate. To tessellate is to tile a plane leaving no spaces. It's amazing to see the variety of shapes that create these interesting patterns.

Home Work

Tessellations Around About

Tessellations are all around us. You've probably walked by tessellation patterns many times without thinking about them. This week look for tessellation patterns in floors, wallpaper, fabric, art, buildings, and more.

1. Locate at least four tessellation patterns.

2. Write about or sketch the polygon that is used to create each pattern.

3. Tell where you found the tessellation.

4. Tell what purpose the tessellation served.

Name _____

About Your Week

Tessellation Art
Creating Tessellation Designs

What you will do:

- Change Polygon Tiles to create new shapes that will tessellate.

- Use unique shapes to create tessellation designs.

- Create more tessellation designs using isometric dot paper.

- Write brief reports about what you have learned about tessellations and the shapes that make them.

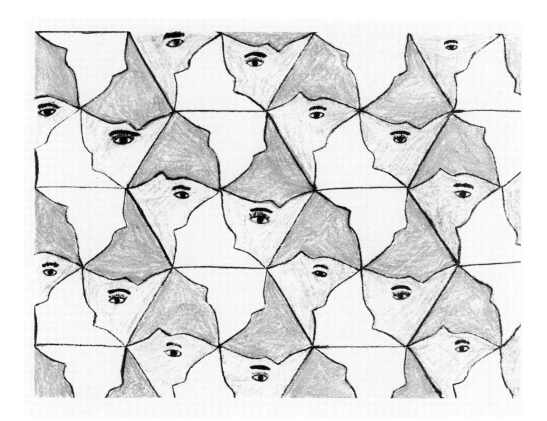

Name _____   Date Due _____

Dear Student,

For the last couple of weeks we have been extending our learning about angles with an investigation of shapes that tessellate. This week our focus is on altering some basic shapes to create unique tessellating shapes. It's amazing to see the patterns and designs that emerge.

Home Work

Tessellation Art

Make your own tessellating design.

1. Cut out or trace one of the shapes shown.

2. Cut a piece from one side and tape the cutout section to the opposite side.

3. Trace your new shape and create a tessellating design with it.

4. Ask one or more family members what the shape reminds them of and decorate the shape appropriately.

5. Try to use color to emphasize your pattern.

6. If other family members have time, suggest that they try making their own unique designs.

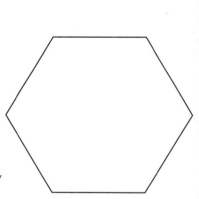

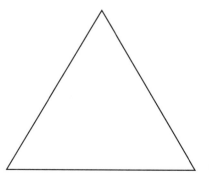

Isometric Dot Paper

Isometric Dot Paper

Name _____   Date _____

1. Which of these is a proper fraction?

A $\frac{8}{5}$

B $1\frac{3}{5}$

C $\frac{4}{8}$

2. Write this mixed number as an improper fraction.

$3\frac{3}{4}$ _____

3. If there is 84¢ altogether, what coins could be covered? _____

4. How much is $\frac{7}{20}$ of a dollar? _____

5. Write the number that comes just after this one.

389,999   _____

6. Circle the number that is more than $\frac{1}{2}$.

$\frac{4}{10}$ $\qquad$ $\frac{5}{12}$ $\qquad$ $\frac{3}{5}$

7. Write this improper fraction as a mixed number.

$\frac{14}{3}$ _____

8. Write two numbers the answer is between.

$487 \div 20 =$ ☐ _____ _____

9. How is 32,408,691 read?
   A thirty two million, four hundred eight thousand, six hundred ninety-one
   B three hundred twenty-four million, eight thousand, six hundred ninety-one
   C thirty two million, forty-eight thousand, six hundred ninety-one

10. Which graph best describes this situation? _____
    There are equal numbers of sixth, seventh, and eighth graders at Parch Middle School.

A

B

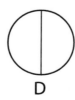
C

D

MathLand® Student Resource Book • Grade 5—23511
© Creative Publications

Name _____ Date _____

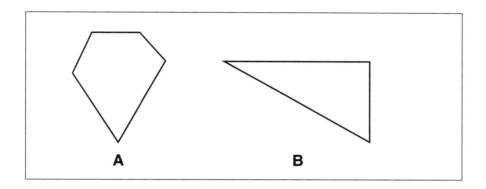

A   B

1. Name each of these polygons. Polygon A: _____ Polygon B: _____

2. Find the measure of each of the angles of these polygons. In the space below each answer, explain how you figured these measures out.

    The angles in Polygon A are: _____

    The angles in Polygon B are: _____

3. For each polygon, what is the sum of all of the angles?

    The sum of the angles in Polygon A is: _____

    The sum of the angles in Polygon B is: _____

Q52 MathLand® Student Resource Book • Grade 5—23511
© Creative Publications

Write the definition and make a sketch to go with each term.

4. Scalene triangle

5. Right triangle

6. Isosceles triangle

MathLand® Student Resource Book • Grade 5—23511
© Creative Publications

Q53 To the teacher: Permission is granted to reproduce this page.

Unit Review **188**

Find the missing angle measure. Tell whether it is right, acute, or obtuse.

7.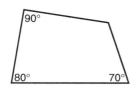

Angle measure: _____

Angle type: _____

8.

Angle measure: _____

Angle type: _____

9.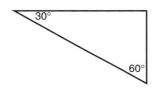

Angle measure: _____

Angle type: _____

10. A triangle has one side that is 4 cm long and one side that is 9 cm long. Which two of the following lengths could the third side be? On another sheet of paper explain your answer using words, numbers, or equations.

○ 3 cm ○ 7 cm ○ 11 cm ○ 15 cm

11. Which of these shapes will tessellate? On another sheet of paper, explain how you know.

   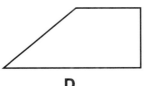

A **B** **C** **D**

○ A ○ B ○ C ○ D

Name _____

Codes and Clues
Exploring Grid Systems Through Puzzles and Games

What you will do:

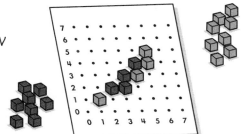

Day Trip One:
- Play a grid game of Tic-Tac-Toe to learn how the coordinate grid system works.

Day Trip Two:
- Crack the code system in a challenging puzzle.

Day Trip Three:
- Use different Rainbow Cubes to represent positive and negative numbers. Examine integer addition by completing an Integer Addition Chart.

Day Trip Four:
- Explore a grid system by using a series of arrows.

Day Trip Five:
- Use your Grid Tic-Tac-Toe coordinate system to play a game of Hidden Shapes with a partner.

Name _____   Date Due _____

Dear Student,

This week you have been looking at different number systems and code systems. At school you solved a Digit Decoders problem. Maybe someone in your family would like to learn how to solve these puzzles, too.

Home Work

Digit Decoders

1. Work with someone in your family to solve the Digit Decoders puzzle shown.

2. Each space in the grid stands for a number 0–9. One number isn't used. Can you figure out which number belongs in each space? Use the equation codes shown to help you. The symbols show the shapes of different grid spaces.

3. Bring in your solutions so you can compare them with the solutions your classmates found.

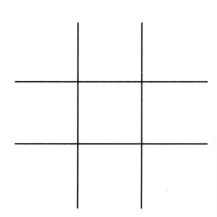

Example:

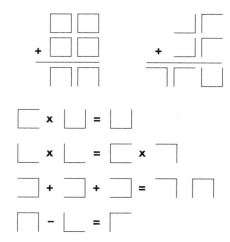

2-cm Dot Paper

2-cm Dot Paper

How to Play Grid-Tac-Toe

How to Play Grid-Tac-Toe

1. Partners need a copy of the Grid-Tac-Toe game board. Each player chooses a different color Rainbow Cube to use as a game marker.

2. One player calls out the pair of numbers that name the dot on which he wishes a cube of his color to be placed. The other player places a cube of her opponent's color in the designated position on the grid.

3. Players take turns calling out a coordinate location on which their opponent then places a cube of their color.

4. The game ends when one player gets 4 in a row (horizontally, vertically, or diagonally). Partners then clear the cubes from the grid and play again.

Grid-Tac-Toe

Name _____

```
7    •    •    •    •    •    •    •    •

6    •    •    •    •    •    •    •    •

5    •    •    •    •    •    •    •    •

4    •    •    •    •    •    •    •    •

3    •    •    •    •    •    •    •    •

2    •    •    •    •    •    •    •    •

1    •    •    •    •    •    •    •    •

0    •    •    •    •    •    •    •    •

     0    1    2    3    4    5    6    7
```

How to Play Four in a Row, High or Low

1. Partners use the 4 × 4 game board. Each partner chooses a different color of Rainbow Cube.

2. Play proceeds as for Grid-Tac-Toe, except that cubes may be stacked on top of one another.

3. The winner is the first to get 4 of his cubes in a row—horizontally, vertically, stacked, or diagonally. (A diagonal "staircase" of 4 steps counts.)

Four in a Row, High or Low

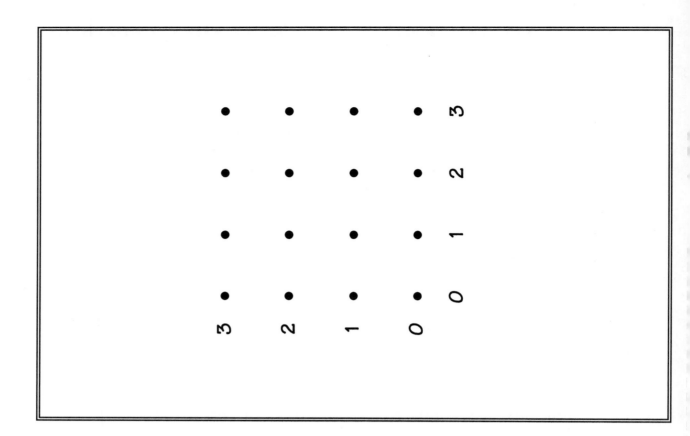

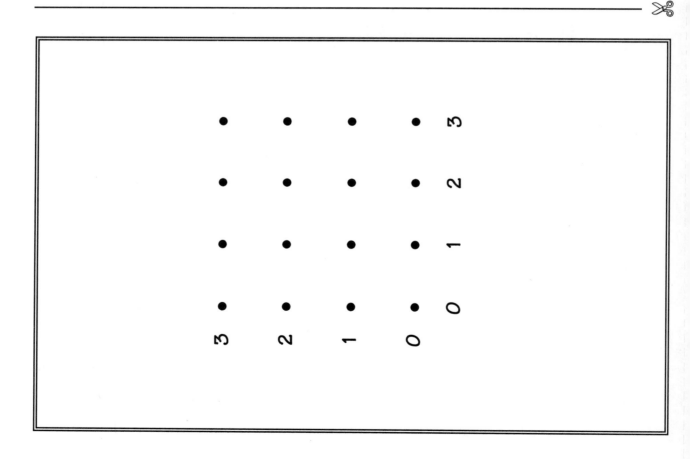

Digit Decoders I

Each space in the grid at left stands for a number 0 – 8. Can you figure out which number belongs in each space? Use the equation codes below to help you. The symbols show the shapes of different grid spaces.

Example:

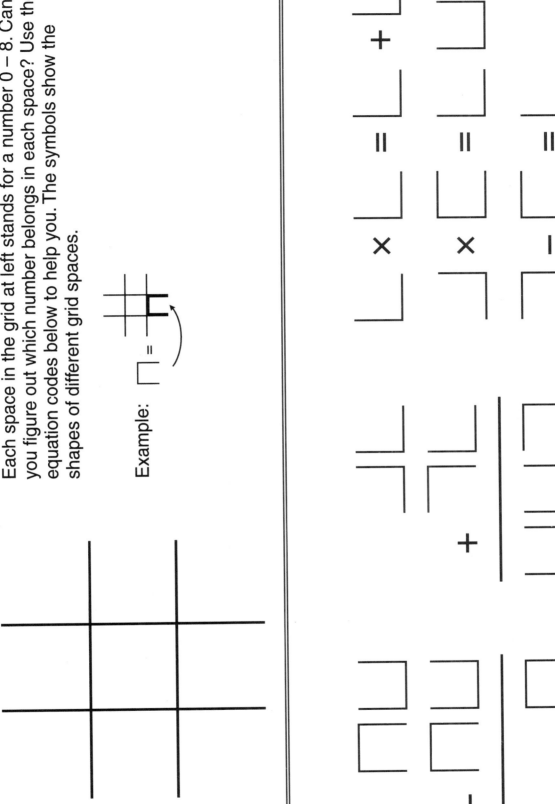

Digit Decoders II

Each space in the grid at left stands for a number 0 – 9. One number is not used. Can you figure out which number belongs in each space? Use the equation codes below to help you. The symbols show the shapes of different grid spaces.

Example:

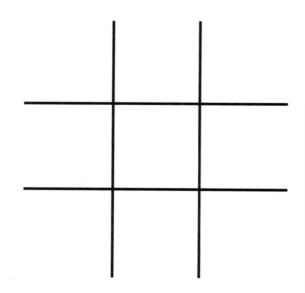

Integer Addition Chart

Name _____

+	-3	-2	-1	0	1	2	3
-3							
-2							
-1							
0							
1							
2							
3							

MathLand® Student Resource Book • Grade 5—23511
© Creative Publications

Grid-Tac-Toe

Name _____

Hidden Shapes

You Will Need

- 2 players
- a Grid-Tac-Toe game board (2-cm dot paper, *Resource Manager,* page A6)
- book or file folder to use as a "wall"

1. Each player secretly draws the following shapes on her grid: a 1 x 1 square, a 1 x 2 rectangle, and a right triangle of base and height 1. Players keep their grids hidden.

2. In turn, players try to locate vertices of their opponent's shapes by guessing coordinate pairs. The opposing player tells if the guess is correct. Players must make up their own systems to keep track of whether or not each guess was correct.

3. When a player thinks she knows all vertices of an opponent's shape, she names the coordinates and tells the shape she thinks she has found.

4. The first player to locate all three of the hidden shapes is the winner.

Numbers Around the World
Analyzing Historical Number Systems

What you will do:

- Learn about a number system developed by another fifth grader.

- Explore several other number systems, such as: Roman, Egyptian, Babylonian, Mayan, Chinese, Hindu-Arabic, and Thai. Work with a partner to determine how some of these number systems work and use them to translate numbers.

- Write a summary of each system, telling in detail the "rules" and patterns of the system.

Number System Summary

Egyptian

0	1	2	3	4	5	6	7	8	9
no zero	I	II	III	IIII	III / II	III / III	IIII / III	IIII / III	IIII / IIIII

10	20	30	40	50	60	70	80	90
∩	∩∩	∩∩∩	∩∩∩ / ∩	∩∩∩ / ∩∩	∩∩∩ / ∩∩∩	∩∩∩ / ∩∩∩ / ∩	∩∩∩∩ / ∩∩∩∩	∩∩∩ / ∩∩∩ / ∩∩∩

Name _____

Date Due _____

Dear Student,

This week you have been exploring some other number systems and trying to figure out how they work. One of the first uses for the ancient number systems was to help people keep inventory. This week choose one of the number systems and use it to conduct an inventory at home.

Home Work

Household Inventory

1. Choose a category of things to count.

2. Decide on a way to sort the items in that category into subsets. For instance, your category might be furniture and your subsets might be chairs, tables, beds, dressers, and so on. Other category ideas include toys, eating utensils, books, and clothing.

3. Conduct an inventory of your category by counting the number of items in each subset. Record your numbers using one of the number systems you learned this week. Use the summary sheet provided by your teacher. Bring your inventory list to school. See if other students can read your numbers.

Furniture

____ chairs

____ tables

____ beds

____ dressers

---

10 x 10 Grid

10 x 10 Grid

Number System Explorations

1. Choose a number system. Take a summary sheet from the envelope for that system.

2. Examine the summary sheet. See if you can understand how the system works. Fill in any missing numbers.

3. Use grid paper to make a 1 to 100 chart for the number system.

4. Solve the Mystery Numerals at the bottom of your summary sheet.

5. How would you write these numbers in the system?
   - the current year
   - your address
   - the year you were born

6. Write about how the system works. Can you think of any advantages or disadvantages of the system?

10 x 10 Grid

About Your Week

Binary Bits
Investigating the Binary Number System

What you will do:

- Make measuring sticks based on the doubling sequence of numbers. Find stick combinations to measure consecutive lengths.

- Learn about the binary number system used in computers, a number system based on the doubling sequence. Build and chart the binary number sequence.

- Try out a color-coded number system based on the number five.

1	10	11	100	101	110	111	1000	1001	1010
1011	1100	1101	1110	1111	10000	10001	10010	10011	10100
10101	10110	10111	11000	11001	11010	11011	11100	11101	11110
11111	100000	100001	100010	100011	100100	100101	100110	100111	101000
101001	101010	101011	101100	101101	101110	101111	110000	110001	110010

Family Letter

Name _____   Date Due _____

Dear Student,

This week you have been busy deciphering the binary, or base-two, number system. You have learned that writing numerals in binary code can get pretty tricky.

Home Work

Hexagram Counting

Here's a set of ancient Chinese figures called *hexagrams*. They're related to the binary system. Can you figure out how the hexagrams work? (**Hint:** Hexagrams are very similar to binary numerals.)

1. Look at the hexagram figures below.

2. Each one stands for a number, zero through seven.

3. Can you figure out how the system works?

4. What do broken lines stand for?

5. What do solid lines stand for?

6. Write about how the hexagrams work, then add the next ten figures to the series of bar diagrams.

7. Challenge: What's the greatest number that can be shown in this system? How do you know?

| 0 | 1 | 2 | 3 | 4 | 5 | 6 | 7 |

20 × 20 cm Grid

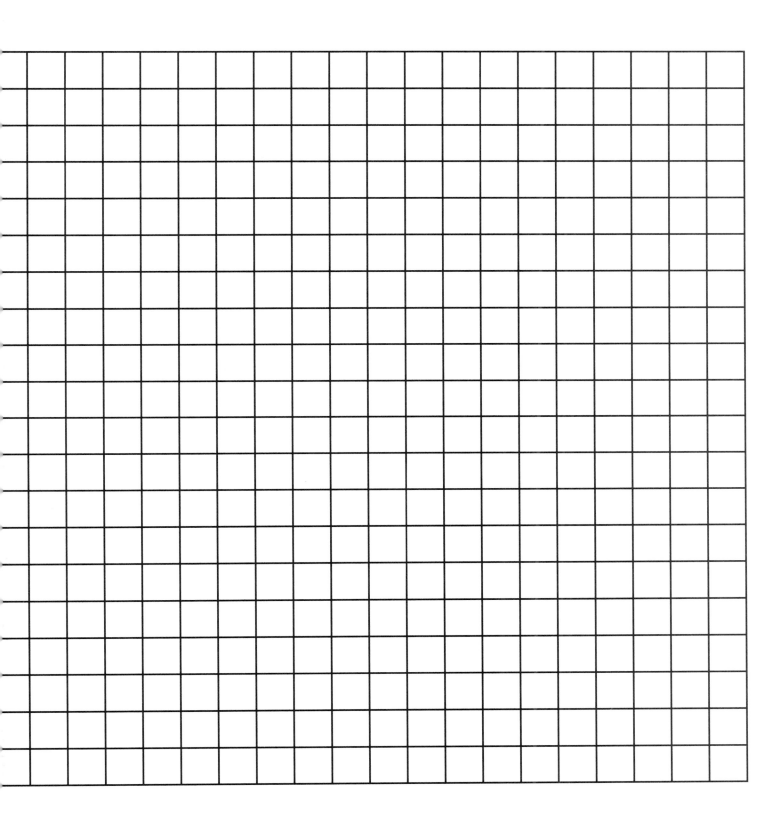

20 × 20 cm Grid

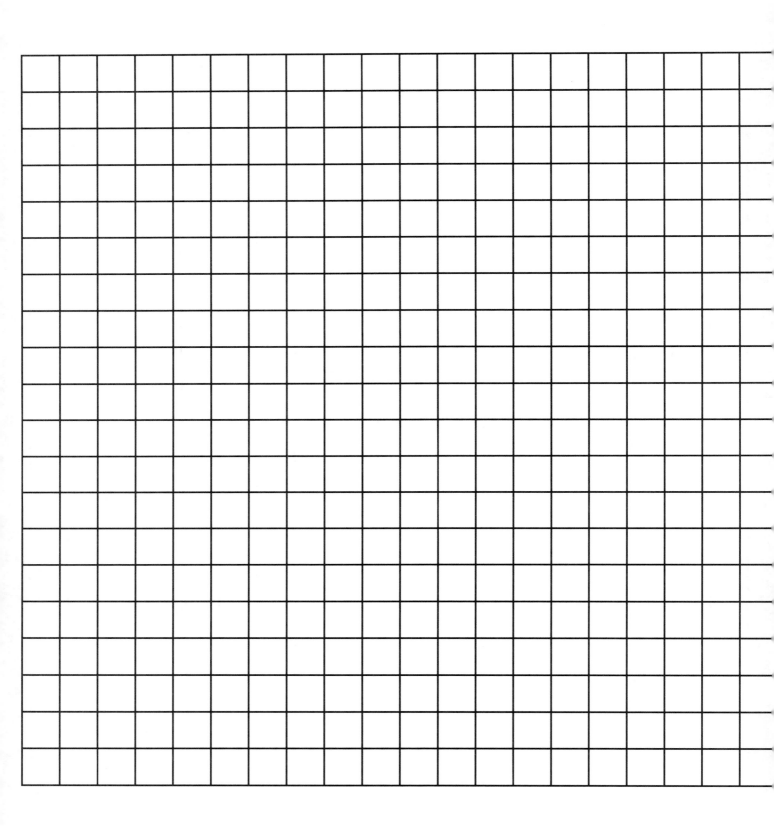

Name _____

About Your Week

Number Systems Expo
Developing and Testing Original Number Systems

What you will do:

- Work with a partner to invent and test a number system that you both will create.

- Write a summary of your number system so that it may be understood by your classmates. Exchange number systems with another pair of your classmates and try out each other's systems.

- Evaluate your classmates' system and make constructive comments about it.

- Examine the comments your classmates make about your system and decide whether you need to revise your system to improve it.

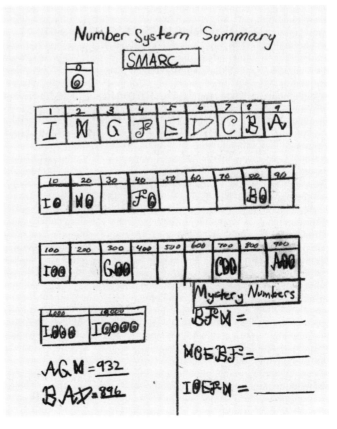

Family Letter

Name _____   Date Due _____

Dear Student,

This week you've been making up some number systems of your own. You've put a lot of thought into your systems and have tried to make them clear to others. Take a copy of your Number System Summary sheet home with you this week so that your family can see your invention.

What do you think about my number system?

Home Work

Number System Workshop

1. Have an older family member look at your summary. Can that person figure out your system well enough to fill in the missing numbers and the Mystery Numbers?

2. Ask that person to write some comments or suggestions for your system.

3. Bring the comments back to school. You can use them on the last day of this project to help you evaluate your system.

Inventing a Number System: Project Guide

Level 1: Design Your System

Invent a number system.

1. How will it work?
2. How will your numerals look?
3. How will your numerals work together to show bigger numbers?

Level 2: Test and Revise Your System

Test your system. Make changes, where necessary, to make your system better.

1. Is your system understandable? (If it's too complicated for anyone to figure out, it's not useful.)
2. Can you write any number with your system?
3. Are there certain numbers in your system that are of key importance?
4. How high does your system go?
5. Is there more than one way to write each number?

Level 3: Write a Number System Summary

Make a Number System Summary sheet for your system like the ones you used to explore the ancient number systems.

1. Think of a name for your system.
2. Make a chart that shows how to write some of the key numerals in your system. Leave some numbers out for your classmates to complete later this week.
3. Include any special notes you need to help explain any complicated parts of your system.
4. Write a few Mystery Numbers in your system for your classmates to decode later this week.
5. Write your name and your partner's name on the back of your summary sheet. For now, your system should be anonymous.

Points to Ponder

- Is the system understandable?

- Is the system easy to use?

- Is it complete? Can you write any number with this system?

- Are any numbers impossible to write?

- Are there any numbers that you can write in more than one way?

- Does the system have an ending?

- What are the advantages and disadvantages of this system?

- Is there anything you'd change to make the system better?

Name _____   Date _____

1. Write a multiplication equation the blocks show. _____

    ▭▭ ▫▫▫
    ▭▭ ▫▫▫
    ▭▭ ▫▫▫
    ▭▭ ▫▫▫

2. Write the number that is 100,000 more than 15,049. _____

3. What number comes next?

99,996   99,998   100,000   _____

4. What number is missing?

1, 3, 6, 10, _____, 21

5. How many 100s are in 10,000,000? _____

6. Estimate the measure of this angle. _____

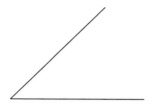

7. Which fraction is greater than $\frac{1}{2}$?

A $\frac{6}{11}$

B $\frac{6}{13}$

C $\frac{7}{14}$

8. If you multiply this number by itself and subtract 7 you get 57.

What is the number? _____

9. How many inches are there in $4\frac{1}{2}$ feet? _____

10. In the circles, write the signs that make the equation true.

(40 ◯ 8) ◯ 4 = 8

Name _____   Date _____

In each set of problems, the symbols represent 1, 2, 3, 4, and 5. Which symbol equals which number in each set?

1. ▌ = _____   ♟ = _____   ▱ = _____   ▽ = _____   ❯ = _____

> ♟ + ▱ = ▌   ▽ − ❯ = ♟
>
> ▽ × ♟ = ▽   ▽ − ▌ = ▱

2. ⬠ = _____   ✦ = _____   ▢ = _____   ◁ = _____   ▲ = _____

> ◁ − ▲ = ✦   ⬠ − ▢ = ✦
>
> ▢ + ▢ = ▢ × ▲   ⬠ ÷ ▲ = ▲

Solve these addition problems. On another sheet of paper, write an explanation for how you solved each problem.

3. $^-4 + {}^-2 =$ _____

4. $^-6 + 4 =$ _____

5. $^-4 + 7 =$ _____

Use this binary system chart to answer questions 6 and 7 on the next page.

64	32	16	8	4	2	1	Make
						1	1
					1	0	2
					1	1	3
				1	0	0	4
				1	0	1	5
				1	1	0	6
							7
							8
							9

Q56 MathLand® Student Resource Book • Grade 5—23511
© Creative Publications

6. How would you write the number 12 in binary code? _____
   Explain how you know.

7. How would you write the number 50 in binary code? _____
   Explain how you know.

Translate these Roman numerals into numbers in our number system.

8. LXXIV = _____

9. MXCVII = _____

Roman									
0	1	2	3	4	5	6	7	8	9
no zero	I	II	III	IV	V	VI	VII	VIII	IX

10	20	30	40	50	60	70	80	90
X	XX	XXX	XL	L	LX	LXX	LXXX	XC

100	200	300	400	500	600	700	800	900
C	CC	CCC	CD	D	DC	DCC	DCCC	CM

1,000	10,000	100,000	Million or Infinity
M	$\overline{X}$	$\overline{C}$	∞

MathLand® Student Resource Book • Grade 5—23511
© Creative Publications

Q57

To the teacher: Permission is granted to reproduce this page.

Unit Review **223**

Predictions
Using Sampling to Make Decisions

What you will do:

- Take a sample of Rainbow Cubes from a bag and make a prediction about the total contents of the bag.

- Take a sampling of your classmates to decide what drinks to buy for an all-school party.

- Create "peek bags" to test your prediction skills.

Family Letter

Name _____   Date Due _____

Dear Student,

This week we are taking samples and making predictions based on the data they provide. Sampling helps us determine the contents of a bag without opening it or the number of each kind of drink to buy without asking every student.

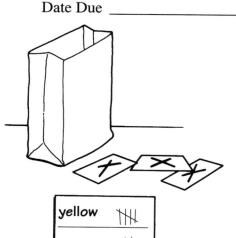

Home Work

An Ample Sample

Carry out this sampling experiment for yourself at home this week.

1. Put a colored X on 100 slips of paper. Use four or five colors.

2. Put the slips of paper in a bag.

3. Take out a 20-slip sample and record the results. Put the slips back in the bag.

4. Repeat the sampling process two more times, for a total of three samples.

5. Write about what you found out.

6. Show your experiment to someone in your family.

7. Write about that person's thinking.

MathLand® Student Resource Book • Grade 5—23511
© Creative Publications

Possible Outcomes
Gaining Confidence in Decision Making

What you will *do:*

Day Trip One:
- Come up with all the possible two-card combinations you can find with the cards ace through 10.

Day Trip Two:
- Play an odd-even game with a pack of ten cards and determine the "fairness" of the game.

Day Trip Three:
- Play a more or less game with the pack of ten cards and determine if two players have an equal chance of winning.

Day Trip Four:
- Apply your skills in determining possible outcomes to a game of rolling the dice.

Day Trip Five:
- Play another dice game and decide if the game is stacked in one player's favor.

Family Letter

Name _____   Date Due _____

Dear Student,

This week we are making predictions by first looking at the possible outcomes. Knowing what is possible helps determine the probability of a certain event's occurring.

Home Work

Three-Coin Combinations

Find a penny, nickel, and dime that you can use to help you think about this probability question. If you flipped these three coins 16 times, how many times do you think you would get heads on all three coins at the same time?

1. First determine all the possible outcomes if you flipped the three coins.

2. Then flip the coins 16 times and record your results.

3. How do your results compare to your prediction? Why do you think that is? Write about it.

MathLand® Student Resource Book • Grade 5—23511
© Creative Publications

Odd or Even?

You Will Need
- 2 players
- 10 playing cards (ace through 10)

1. Shuffle the cards and deal 5 cards, face down, to each player. Decide who will play for "odds" and who will play for "evens."

2. Each player turns one card face up. If the sum of the two cards is an even number, the player who chose evens scores a point. If the sum is an odd number, the player who chose odds scores a point.

3. Continue until all the cards have been played. The winner of the round is the player with the most points.

More or Less?

You Will Need
- 2 players
- deck of cards (ace through 10)

1. Shuffle the deck and deal 5 cards, face down, to each player. Decide who will play for sums more than 10 and who will play for sums less than or equal to 10.

2. Each player turns one card face up. If the sum of the numbers is 10 or less, that player gets a point. If the sum of the numbers is more than 10, that player gets a point.

3. Players continue until all the cards have been played. The winner is the player with the most points.

Let 'Em Roll

You Will Need
- 2 players
- 2 dice

1. Players decide who will play for "odds" and who will play for "evens."

2. Players take turns rolling the dice. If the sum is an odd number, the player who chose odds gets a point. If the sum is even, the player who chose evens gets a point.

3. The winner is the player with the most points at the end of twenty rounds.

Name _____   Date _____

1. How many 1000s are in 1,000,000? _____

2. Write the correct sign, > or <, to show which number is greater.

   60,991 ◯ 61,119

3. If a yard is 3 feet, how many inches are in $1\frac{1}{2}$ yards? _____

4. Write an improper fraction with 4 as the denominator. _____

5. Write an improper fraction with 4 as the numerator. _____

6. How many 10,000s in 100,000? _____

7. How many 1,000,000s in 20,000,000? _____

8. If you subtract 30 from this number and multiply the result by 7 you get 42.

   What is the number? _____

9. Write this improper fraction as a mixed number.

   $\frac{17}{6}$ _____

10. What is $\frac{3}{5}$ of 25? _____

Name _____   Date _____

There are 600 students at June's school. Some of them were surveyed to find out how they wanted to spend the money they made in their school fair. Each student surveyed was asked to make only one choice. Here are the survey results:

Survey Results: How Should We Spend Our Money?

Playground equipment	42 votes
New books for the library	13 votes
A school garden	10 votes

---

1. About what fraction of the school took part in the survey? _____

2. Using the survey as a sample, predict what the results might be if all 600 students voted. Use words and numbers to explain how you predicted.

Votes for playground equipment: _____

Votes for new library books: _____

Votes for a school garden: _____

Record your answers to problems 3–5 on another sheet of paper.

3. What are all the two-card combinations you can make with these cards?

4. Explain how you made sure that you found all the possible combinations without repeating or missing any of them.

5. June and Emilio played the "Odd or Even" game with the ten cards above. June got a point if the sum of the two cards was odd. Emilio got a point if the sum of the two cards was even. Explain whom you would expect to win. Use words, pictures, or numbers to explain your thinking.

MathLand® Student Resource Book • Grade 5—23511
© Creative Publications

⟨Q59⟩

Unit Review **236**
To the teacher: Permission is granted to reproduce this page.

Computation Check ◇ 4

Name _____ Date _____

Solve these problems as quickly as you can. Use the strategies that work best for you.

1. $180° + 180° =$ _____

2. $\$100.00 \div \$0.50 =$ _____

3. $1\frac{3}{4} + 3\frac{1}{2} =$ _____

4. $245 + 199 + 50 =$ _____

5. $\$10.00 \div 5 =$ _____

6. $30° + 60° + 90° =$ _____

7. $90° + 270° =$ _____

8. $\frac{2}{5} + \frac{1}{3} + \frac{1}{6} =$ _____

9. $7\overline{)\$8.61}$

10. $\frac{5}{2} + \frac{3}{4} =$ _____

11. $\frac{1}{4} \times 20 =$ _____

12. $8 \times \frac{2}{5} =$ _____

13. $\frac{3}{5} - \frac{1}{4} =$ _____

14. $\frac{2}{5} + \frac{1}{3} + \frac{4}{6} =$ _____

15. $\begin{array}{r} 1\frac{3}{8} \\ - \frac{7}{8} \\ \hline \end{array}$

16. $\begin{array}{r} 143 \\ \times\ 94 \\ \hline \end{array}$

17. $\begin{array}{r} 135° \\ -\ 90° \\ \hline \end{array}$

18. $\begin{array}{r} 6837 \\ -\ 79 \\ \hline \end{array}$

19. $\begin{array}{r} 3577 \\ 385 \\ +\ 78 \\ \hline \end{array}$

20. $\begin{array}{r} \$75.55 \\ \times\ 7 \\ \hline \end{array}$

MathLand Certificate

This is to certify that _____

NAME

and family have completed the

MathLand® Journey for Grade Five.

Good Work!

_____

TEACHER

5

JOURNEYS ★ THROUGH MATHEMATICS